*Best wishes*

*John Pickersgill*

# LOOKING FOR THE REAL ME

John Pickersgill

MINERVA PRESS

LONDON

MIAMI DELHI SYDNEY

LOOKING FOR THE REAL ME
Copyright © John Pickersgill 2000

ISBN  0  75411  298  5

First Published 2000 by
MINERVA PRESS
315–317 Regent Street
London W1R 7YB

Printed in Great Britain for Minerva Press

# LOOKING FOR THE REAL ME

*To Beatrice, Bridgett and Susie*

# Chapter I

## EARLY DAYS

A thick swirl of fog curled up around the gaslight and disappeared into the cold night air. I thought to myself, This is what is called a pea-souper. I wasn't quite sure what it meant, but I had heard my mother use the phrase and I somehow associated it with the North of England and the thick black smoke that emanated from the factories and engine sheds in and around the Manchester suburbs.

There were not many gaslights left in Kirk Street, as they were gradually being replaced by electric ones. These were much taller and encased in laminate, which prevented their bulbs from being shattered when the unruly element in the neighbourhood threw stones up at them. Those that remained certainly showed how antiquated they had become – a remnant of the late Forties and early Fifties.

Tomorrow was another Sunday, and we would go to mass at the Sacred Heart. I hated it. I would be made to get up at some godforsaken hour, when I preferred lying in a nice warm bed. What was the objective of this exercise? The objective was to listen to some old man – the priest, usually Irish – droning on in a monotone voice about the Virgin Mary and Jesus, people whom I had never met at the tender age of four and therefore in whom I had not the slightest interest. Two things made these visits worse. First, my mum and dad told me that I had to believe in these two characters, and, secondly, my knees used to hurt when I knelt on the kneeler. Also, I could never understand why my mum went out of her way to pay such great homage to the priest after the service, as if he were some *saint* himself.

None of the other boys and girls I played with in the vicinity of our home ever had to go to church on a Sunday, or any other day for that matter. They seemed to have what I felt was a normal life, and I began to feel that I was slightly different from these playmates, a feeling I didn't like. Most of the families in the neighbourhood were non-Catholics and we were Catholics.

My friends would ask me what went on at this church and I couldn't think of a satisfactory answer – it was evident that we were one thing and they were another. In essence they were Prodidogs and we were Catlicks, but my mum and indeed my grandfather, on my mum's side, always strove to point out that we were somehow the better types. It was almost as though a conflict existed, albeit an imaginary one. On the occasions Catholicism *was* mentioned, which appeared to be a lot, I became uneasy. I didn't want to be at odds with anyone, least of all my friends, whoever they might be. The one thing I liked in my life was harmony, not discord.

One day, however, I was walking home from school, up the steep part of Kirk Street, when I caused my own disharmony. I swallowed a marble. It was not a big deal, but at five years of age I was frightened. I thought I was going to die before I reached the house. I made it home. So far so good, but how much longer had I got? I was in tears. 'What's the matter?' asked my mum.

I told her and as she didn't appear too concerned, I began to calm down.

'It's no problem,' she explained, 'you will get rid of it when you go to the toilet. If you keep an eye out you will be able to see the marble, and that will put your mind at ease.'

I didn't intend to keep an eye out – I just didn't want any pain! Above all else, I was pleased that I wasn't going to die.

The nominal head of my circle of friends near home was a huge fat slob called David Ratcliffe. He was older, confident, loud and very bossy. Any games which involved running and athleticism were just up my street, despite my diminutive size, but this guy would not let anyone take the lead except himself and would verbally castigate anyone trying to do so. I knew I was better at most games than he was, and I seemed to form a determined resolve to 'prove myself'. However, all his ordering me about, coupled with his remarks about Catholics, left me uneasy. But if I felt uneasy then, that was nothing compared to what was to come.

I arrived home one day and my mum asked me how school was.

'It's fine,' I replied.

'Good. How do you get on with the other children in class?'

'Very well,' I replied, which was true.

'Well, I just want you to know that we love you just as much as those parents love their children, but we are not actually your real parents.'

I was speechless, and, for the first time I could ever remember, confused. What did all this mean? Before I could think what to say my mum continued. 'Your real mother didn't want you and we adopted you.'

It felt as if a sledgehammer had struck me. I could not understand how anyone could have parents who were not real. Turmoil abounded in my mind. Now I was different from the others but for all the wrong reasons.

Days and weeks went by. I was distracted by the things that distract young children, but the words would come back to haunt me, often when I least expected it. How could my real mother have given me away, and why? I wasn't ugly, deformed or a problem to anybody! I began to have nightmares on a regular basis. It was always the same dream. I was on horseback, or I was the horse – I could never work out which – and I would gallop towards the finishing post. With every stride forward the intensity would build up to such a pitch that I would become horribly frightened. As I crossed the line I would wake up screaming and punching the air with tears streaming down my cheeks. Occasionally I would have these frightening experiences when we had visitors, and they would appear visibly disturbed. They would comment to my parents that this was unnatural. I could assure them that it was not. I also began sucking my thumb.

I began to have deep, deep thoughts. I had lots of aunts and uncles and at this stage several cousins. If my parents were not 'Real Parents', then these relations must be foreign to me also. What does a boy of six do when he discovers that all the people closest to him are complete strangers? Inwardly he panics and, overnight, he becomes lost in himself.

# Chapter II
# NEW BEGINNINGS

In the summer of 1953 we moved several miles away to a new house. My parents sold the confectionery shop and my mother found a new job in an office in Manchester. For me this meant a new school and, I hoped, a new set of pals who would be that bit friendlier. This time the school was St Josephs, a good, solid, mixed Catholic school with a reputation for academic achievement and a set of teachers to challenge the mind on the dullest of days. I had only been there a few months when fate was to dish out another of its quirks.

It was a close, rainy day in July. I could see through the classroom window that it had started to rain again. It always rained in Manchester, or so it seemed. The teacher was covering certain historical facts. She was explaining how, in days gone by, newborn infants had been left on doorsteps. She described them as 'Foundlings'. Nothing in this statement unduly concerned me until she mentioned that these children were usually placed in homes for adoption. At this point I felt my heart race and experienced a rush of emotion as she calmly announced that such children do not actually have real parents – they have adopted parents. I was trembling inside and then I became angry, but I was not sure why. I wanted to say something, but I couldn't. I suddenly decided that the teacher had no right to refer to this topic because it felt like an intrusion. It was beginning to cause me anguish, if not pain. She carried on nonchalantly, as if such matters were an everyday occurrence. As an afterthought, she said to the class, 'These things hardly ever happen nowadays and are a thing of the past.'

I almost shouted out loudly, 'What things?' But I held my tongue. So my adoption was now referred to as a 'thing', or was I the 'thing'?

I wanted to refer this to a higher authority, but I was young and I didn't have the nerve. In any case, to whom would I refer it? The headmaster was an intelligent but rather eccentric person. What sort of man kept a selection of canes hidden away in his cupboard? There was a collection of about twenty, ranging in thickness from thin to very thin and thick to very thick. His choice of implement would depend on his mood, and indeed on whom he was about to mete out the punishment to. I remembered one particular incident quite clearly. My best friend Charles had been talking in class and was about to receive punishment. This headmaster instructed my friend to select a cane himself. As my friend did so, the headmaster turned to him with a look of sympathy. 'Not that one boy, that one will kill you,' he said, and promptly selected an implement himself, which was much thinner and therefore less likely to inflict so much pain! On top of that, he would never punish the girls, no matter how offensive they were. He would expect a boy to volunteer to take a girl's punishment. Naturally enough, there were hardly any volunteers to take four strokes of the cane on behalf of someone else, let alone a girl. He was regarded throughout the school as 'odd'; some even said he was 'sadistic'.

'You must never take the cane to a young lady,' he would often say, 'as this could inflict serious harm on such delicate and soft tissue, a young lady's skin is not designed to receive such harsh treatment.'

However, when it came to the boys that was a different matter. He seemed to take a great delight in describing the different ways that the males withstood their punishment. For example he would refer to one pupil as 'a weakling'.

'Master Burke you often behave in a belligerent manner and you seem to think it amusing. You always look around at your classmates to see if they are laughing with you. Well, I can assure you that they are laughing at you, not with you. And then when you take your punishment, instead of behaving like a man, you double up with the pain, like a weakling. If you were a real man, you would take four strokes of the rod and sit down as if nothing had happened.' The class were in 'stitches' after his humiliation and I wondered if the headmaster had ever tried sitting down calmly after receiving four heavy strokes, which quite definitely left you in untold agony for at least twenty minutes. What a leader!

The deputy head would be no use either as he was a cantankerous Irishman with mood swings directly related to the amount of alcohol consumed the previous night. No, I would just have to keep this matter to myself, at least for the time being. Although I didn't realise it, the whole scenario was beginning to tick away inside me, like a time bomb. I didn't feel as if I had anyone to talk to on the matter and I wasn't prepared to bring the subject up at home as I didn't wish to hurt my parents. Instead the problem lay festering in the vaults of my mind.

At seven years of age we were obliged to make our first confession and take Holy Communion, which was a big thing in the eyes of the church and also of my parents. This was supposed to prepare us for eternal life in the future and make us holy in some way. I remember having to prepare myself for confession – you were not allowed to receive communion unless you had first been to the confessional box. So I had to 'examine' my conscience and find some sins I had committed and confess them to the priest. I was nervous and I found this difficult. My first thoughts were directed to the priest. I wondered what sins he could have committed and whether he was made to confess them to a complete stranger. I entered the dark interior of the confessional and mumbled the standard words, 'Bless me, Father, for I have sinned.' The priest then asked me several questions. 'Did I eat meat on Fridays? Did I always go to mass on Sundays? Had I disobeyed my parents? If so, how often?' When this ordeal was over, I, somewhat embarrassed went to recite my penance in another part of the church. Three Hail Marys was my punishment. I had got off lightly. Our teachers told us that the sacraments of 'Holy Confession and Holy Communion' would help guide us throughout our life, and assist us with our everyday problems. This train of thought was reiterated by my parents on a regular basis. Unfortunately for me, my problems had not diminished. Why had not the miraculous 'Jesus' heard my plea and helped me with my troubles? It must have been because I was not worthy, and obviously I needed to work harder at being a good Catholic. I resolved to try harder – then surely I would begin to understand my muddled state of mind. But life wasn't like that. Just before the confession ordeal I wondered if any other person had problems like mine. I very much doubted it. However, one of my classmates appeared to be very agitated and was asking which priest would be the most understanding, as he had committed a sin against holy purity. Under no account should he confess to Father Gannon, as that would be a nightmare. Father Daly was the one to visit. At the appointed time, however, he was ushered into Father Gannon's box, and I took mild consolation from this.

After confession and communion there was a third sacrament for us to receive. This one was entitled 'Confirmation' and involved taking the name of a saint. For example, John Smith could now become John Dominic Smith. Quite what the objective of this event was, I was not sure, but it seemed to be something to do with admitting a person to full church membership. I found this odd, as I thought my Baptism had already done that. Anyhow, we had to select another name and prepare for this in a big way – none other than the 'Bishop' was to preside over the proceedings. Now with all this back-up from the church, surely I would soon be able to consider myself a real person? After all, I was told that if I prayed daily to Jesus, He would resolve all my problems. What more does a boy of seven need to convince him? I was reminded that Jesus was God and that God was everywhere – in your pocket, in the street, in your eyes, in your mouth. The only problem for me was that I couldn't see or taste Him! However, lest I should forget, I was reminded also that He knew everything, including my innermost thoughts. Everything was possible if one believed and put one's faith in God – that is what we were taught. For some strange reason this didn't seem to be holding true for me. If this God person was as reliable as he was supposed to be, why hadn't he told me that I hadn't got real parents? 'Jesus will not forsake anyone' – that was the daily message from our teachers. Well, they were wrong; I felt totally forsaken. The thumb-sucking got worse and I could not understand why my friends or cousins did not have the same affliction. I only did this in private and it was embarrassing enough without it being broadcast in public.

We were visiting my parents' friends and there were other children there too. I had been getting on famously with them and enjoying the day until my mother ruined it all in one fell swoop. Their friends were asking about me, as parents do.

'How has he settled?'

'Oh, fine,' replied my mother. 'He is a good lad.' She cast a sideways glance in my direction and then addressed me: 'You only have one problem, don't you?'

I wasn't sure what was coming next. I squirmed inside. What now? I thought.

'He is nine years of age and he still sucks his thumb.' I felt tears well up in my eyes. The whole room fell silent and the other children stared at me. I felt crushed by this latest blow.

How insensitive could she get? Revealing this innermost secret was bad enough, but to do so in front of all these people was devastating. Her friend broke the silence.

'I wonder why he does it – is he craving for something?' If I was craving for something then perhaps it was help, or comfort I wasn't really sure.

Back at St Joseph's the daily routine unfolded, always in the same dreary manner. There would be a barrel-load of prayers at 9 a.m. The morning lessons would be interspersed with mathematics and the inevitable 'Religion'. Then at twelve noon there were more prayers before we departed for lunch. From time to time the parish priest would visit each class. This would be a time of great merriment or despair, depending upon whose point of view one took. The current parish priest was a frustrated Irish stickler, who demanded correct, quick-fire responses to any question he posed on the Catholic religion. Woe betide anyone who got them wrong! If you gave a wrong answer you were in for big trouble from him, followed by another blasting from the deputy head, for having let both yourself and the school down.

Father Gannon was in no mood for compromise one morning. His first order was to ask one boy to recite the 'Act of Contrition'. He failed miserably, and began blushing and then stammering. Gannon was furious. His next target was a tall lumbering lad who had a reputation for being awkward at the best of times.

'Do you believe in God, boy?'

'No,' was the response.

'No what?' asked Gannon, fuming.

'No, I don't believe in God.'

'How dare you – you will reply to me in a proper manner. My title is Father, Father Gannon. Do you understand? Now, I ask you again: do you believe in God?'

There was a stunned silence.

'No, I do not believe in God.'

The class was gripped in fear and apprehension. By now, Gannon's cheeks were bright red and he was so enraged that spittle was protruding from the corner of his mouth. He exploded, first to the boy and then to Mr Guiton. 'You are damned, boy; hellfire and brimstone await you. Mr Guiton, what is this heathen doing in my school?' He stormed out towards the headmaster's office, mumbling along the way, 'What is this school coming to?'

Some of the class were giggling; some were terrified. I sat there inwardly smiling, glad that this had happened to some other poor sod and not me! What is that proverb? 'Let he who is without sin cast the first stone'. Was Jesus about to teach me a harsh lesson?

The 'Church' always celebrated the feast days of the saints and martyrs. The feast of St Bernadette was no different. It was the month of May and once again Father Gannon appeared in the classroom with his usual vigour. We wondered upon whom he was likely to pick on this time; however, for once he addressed his question to the class as a whole, in his broad Irish accent.

'Now children, who was burnt to death?'

Quick as a flash and not to be outdone by anyone this time, I answered, 'Joan of Arc, Father.'

'Joan of Arc! For God's sake, what sort of an answer is that?'

I felt my cheeks turn rapidly red and then crimson. People were laughing at me and I felt totally stupid; I fought to hold back the tears, which on this occasion I managed to do. Gannon was now bellowing at Mr Guiton, 'What are you teaching them in this school, Mr Guiton?' Without waiting for a reply, he stormed out. Then the penny dropped. It was his pronounced Irish accent which had confused me. What he had really said was 'Who was

Bernadette?' not, 'Who was burnt to death?' This was another blow to my already fading morale, at a time when I desperately needed a morale booster. But the pendulum appeared to be swinging the opposite way.

In the mid-Fifties a Catholic education was supposed to make you strong in faith, hope and morals, and also help prepare you for adult life. We, as children, were to search our souls and ask God to lead us to our true vocation. To put it another way, we had to find ourselves, and then whatever plans He had for us would somehow miraculously appear. At this age it would have been a miracle if I had even been able to find my way through my eleven plus. I didn't – I failed.

My parents were gutted and mother went down to the town hall to find out why. It was probably a hopeless mission in the first place. They had requested that I attend a Catholic grammar school if I passed. There was a severe shortage of places at the Catholic schools and it was suggested that a place could be found at a non-Catholic school, if my parents so desired. They declined and I felt another dent to my pride.

# Chapter III

# THE MAGIC BOX

We were growing older and morals were the order of the day. The dogmas of the church were drummed into us daily. The constant repetition of prayers and the recital of the catechism were obligatory.

These instruments, together with the sacraments, would help keep us pure and chaste. Above all else we must always avert our eyes from bad books or take them to our parents or teachers. The same philosophy applied to bad companions. We were told that there were three types of companions: good, bad and those who were not wholly bad, nor altogether good. We should choose our companions from amongst the first class, never have anything to do with the second class (the bad) and mix with the last class only when there was a need to do so, but never be on familiar terms with any of them. But who were these bad companions? If we thought about it, we would know who they were.

For example, they were those who were not ashamed to use bad language, scandalous words and expressions with double meanings. They were those who grumbled, told lies, swore, blasphemed; tried to keep you away from church and wanted you to steal and disobey your parents and superiors, or to neglect your duty. All such people were servants of the Devil, and those whom you must shun more than the greatest horror of Satan himself. Now, after listening to this, there wasn't much margin for error, but the one overriding theme which we were constantly reminded of was Holy Purity. The Catholic religion was portrayed as a beacon shinning in the dark. The teaching offered in the schools was supposed to be exemplary, building us into good citizens. Of course, those who took heed of the teachings would glow with pride and, above all else, 'self-esteem'.

There had been a rumour going around for months about one

of the teachers. He was supposed to be 'interfering' with pupils, male pupils. There were so many stories circulating that this had to be true. There was no smoke without fire. Whatever was supposed to have happened had apparently happened in lessons initially, and then later on a one-to-one basis. One day a group of us were discussing this and one of the boys piped up that 'He' had tried it on in the classroom – the teacher, that was. But the boy had managed to protect himself. The stories abounded for months and then one day Father Gannon interviewed one of my friends.

'What is all this rough stuff with Mr Glynn?' he asked.

'Rough stuff, Father, do you mean fighting?'

'You know what I mean, boy. Has Mr Glynn been interfering with you?'

He strenuously denied this, but later he secretly admitted that it was true. The end of term arrived and one by one we were called to the front of the class to have our term work scrutinised by Mr Glynn. When my turn came, I noticed Mr Glynn's half-written letter, addressed to the archbishop, proffering his resignation. When the following term came he was gone! As was usual in a Catholic school, the whole incident was hushed up for fear of damaging the school's image. It wasn't immediately obvious, however, that this sinner was going to burn in hellfire, as he appeared to have got off scot-free. With regard to 'pride and self-esteem', I couldn't find it in my personal life and I couldn't find it at school! I would have to look elsewhere.

There were yearnings stirring deep inside my inner self and I didn't know how to tackle them. However, I had always been a thinker, and more especially in recent times. There had to be a way of finding out more information. If I hadn't got real parents, then there must be some documents appertaining to this. It didn't take a genius to work that out.

One day, around Christmas time, I came upon presents stored in my parents' wardrobe. I realised that they were gifts from my relations. During this investigation I noticed an old money box hidden away at the back. I didn't pay much attention to it at the time, but for some reason made a mental note of it. One Monday, at about six o'clock, I entered my parents' bedroom and nervously opened the wardrobe searching for the box. I half-expected it not to be there, but it was. I pulled it out and it made a jangling sound as I did so. I could see it was old and probably handed down from my grandfather. I was naturally hoping that my hour had come but the damn thing was locked! What now? My hopes were dashed, by a single stroke. My plans would have to be put on hold, until another day. The weeks went by and I kept wondering where the key to this *magic* box was kept. I might not have found the key, but I suddenly found I had an ally: 'Hope': This ally, for now at least, was far better than pride and self-esteem.

It was June again and we as a family went to visit a work colleague of my mother's. These visits were always spent in adult company, as her friend had no children of her own. I never felt out of place – in fact, I seemed to thrive in adult company, though I didn't know why. However, I sometimes got bored and invariably took along a book to occupy my mind. The adults were discussing the usual adult subjects, when Mrs Brown asked if I had many friends.

'I have a few special friends, at school,' I replied.

The next statement was addressed to my parents, but I felt I was being pressurised by Mrs Brown to nod my seal of approval. 'You are a very lucky boy, aren't you?'

I wasn't sure what she was getting at. 'I don't know,' I replied.

'You are a lucky boy,' she continued.

'I don't think I am particularly lucky,' I said.

'Well, if *you* are not lucky, who is?'

As usual, I was just being forthright and honest in my answers, even though I was feeling threatened. As per normal I could feel the tears at the back of my eyes. I felt as if I was being accused of something, but I knew not what. 'Bernard Hornby has a giant electric train set – *he* is lucky. I don't have one at all.'

'Well, you should be grateful for all you have got,' continued Mrs Brown. My mother nodded in agreement.

'I *am* grateful for all I have got, but Bernard Hornby is luckier than I am – he has a train set.'

An atmosphere set in and I could sense that whatever I said would be taken the wrong way. I started to clam up, but at the same time I felt indescribably angry inside and I was unable to vent this anger. If I let my emotions take over I would be in big trouble later, when we headed home. I fell silent, which was probably just as well.

My mother began to speak. 'As I was going to say, we adopted him when we lost two of our own. I had two stillbirths and a miscarriage and we decided that if God didn't want us to have children, then so be it. But he has been a good lad so far and I am sure he appreciates what he has got. You do, don't you, son?'

I was dumbfounded. 'Yes,' I replied. Turmoil abounded again, yet in these last few seconds my anger had subsided and a feeling of curiosity had overtaken my being. This was news to me and I wanted to know more, but I knew I wouldn't have the 'bottle' to raise the subject. Unless they were more forthcoming I felt the topic would be relegated to the bin. Nevertheless I *had* learnt something, even if it had been in an obscure way.

On the journey home though, I was reminded that I had upset Mrs Brown, who felt I didn't appreciate all the good things I had – especially two loving parents. I might have been young, but I was intelligent enough to see that it was my parents who were upset, albeit over nothing. Why suggest it was Mrs Brown, who was upset? Yes, I *did* have loving parents and I loved them too, but cut out all this double-talk! Just say what you mean and mean what you say! The way this incident had unfolded could have left me thinking that I was only a 'substitute son', a mere afterthought without significance, and I knew that this was not the case.

One day when my parents were out I returned to the bedroom to search for the keys to the *magic* box. There was an old jewellery box on the dressing table and underneath an assortment of jewellery I found several keys. Was my luck in? I hoped I would soon find out. I lifted the money box carefully out of the wardrobe. I tried the first key. Too big. I tried the second. Too small. I tried another and this time it fitted. By now I could feel my heart racing. I gently opened the lid, unsure what the contents might reveal. There were several old coins – farthings, silver sixpences and some pennies – and on top of these was a bundle of papers. I was carefully extracting these documents, trying to ensure that my thieving would not be discovered, when I heard a car draw up. My parents had returned! I panicked and stuffed the papers back in the box knowing full well that someone looking inside would see that the contents had been disturbed. Now I had to replace the keys back in the jewellery box. I threw them in and quickly ran to my own room, trying to appear calm.

Twice I had been defeated; I was not going to let this happen a third time. I had to pick my time more carefully. One Sunday my chance arrived. My parents always went to mass at eight o'clock. On this particular morning I was serving as an altar boy at the nine o'clock mass. While they were out I went to work. I methodically removed the papers, keeping them in the same order. There was a small document folded inside a larger one. Bold print stared up at me from the larger parchment, overshadowing the smaller print: IN THE COUNTY BOROUGH OF... I glanced over the whole document, my eyes darting from top to bottom. Then I realised that I needed to read slowly in order to take it all in. At the top of the page it read: 'Adoption order in respect of an infant named John Pickersgill, formerly David O'Neill'. It also gave my mother's name as Bridgett, and the long document basically set out the details of my adoption in very formal words.

I had been hoping that it would tell me a great deal more about myself, but it didn't. The smaller document was a birth certificate showing my name, sex, date of birth and place of birth. So now I had plundered the box, but I still hadn't learnt anything really new, except where I had been born and the date of my adoption. I still knew nothing about my origins. On the exterior, I must have appeared happy enough. I was being brought up in a caring and loving environment, but the thoughts I had harboured for the last seven years were now starting to gnaw away inside my head. Just who was I? Where had I come from? Why was I in this situation? I needed to find the answers.

# Chapter IV

## SEEKING MIRACULOUS INTERVENTION

She was an attractive girl and I really liked her. She also had a number of sisters, at least one of which had been fostered, as far as I could make out, by the very same nuns that had looked after me in my first six weeks of infancy. I could use this fact, I thought, as an easy excuse to get to speak with her. Secondly, I hoped to glean some information, whatever that might be, about the adoption process. In truth, I was hoping she would know, how one went about finding out information about one's past.

The Catholic Rescue Society held fund raising events, such as garden parties, in the summer months. There would be the usual tombola stalls, where participants had the opportunity to win prizes, and lots of other events, all with the sole objective of raising funds for the society. These events were usually held on long hot Saturdays between June and September. Parents would attend with their adoptive and fostered children and Anne would normally be in attendance, carrying her fostered sister on her shoulders. I had tried to get to know her at school, but I was so shy I didn't know how to go about it. Somehow along the way, however, I had written her a love letter which I wanted to give her. As usual, I had lost my nerve and the letter had remained in my pocket until we returned home. I had felt enormously guilty about writing it. I was a twelve-year-old boy putting down on paper my innermost feelings for a girl – even worse, a girl I hardly knew. I felt sure that this was a mortal sin and that if I died tomorrow, without having confessed this to the priest, I was sure to go to hell. Those who die in a state of mortal sin always go to hell. Now this was becoming too much to bear, because the description of hell was frightening. Hell, according to our teachers, was a place destined by Divine Justice for the eternal punishment of those who died in mortal sin. The first pain that the damned suffer in hell is the torment of the senses caused by fire, which burns terribly without ever growing less. Fire in the eyes, fire in the mouth, fire in every part. Each sense suffers in its own particular way. The eyes are blinded by smoke and darkness, and terrified by the sight of demons and other lost souls. The ears hear nothing day and night but continual howling, lamenting and blaspheming. The sense of smell suffers extremely from the suffocating fumes of sulphur and burning pitch. The mouth is afflicted with a burning thirst and a ravenous hunger. Then those unfortunate souls, burning with thirst, devoured by hunger and tormented by fire, will cry out, moaning and despairing, 'What a fearful dungeon of misery. How unhappy they are, who fall into such an abyss!' Now consider also that if you go to hell, you will never leave it. A hundred years will pass, a thousand will go by, and hell will only be beginning. Millions and millions of centuries will pass, and even then hell will only be beginning. The lost soul will see 'Forever' written in the flames that burn him. 'Forever' will be engraved on the blades of the swords that pierce him. 'Forever' will be stamped on the doors closed to him for all eternity. Eternity is a bottomless abyss, a sea without shore, a cavern without escape. After this description, even the most courageous would tremble with fear, and this was for just wanting to talk to a young girl! We arrived back home from the garden party and I realised I had failed in my objective. I hadn't actually spoken with her. I remember being very frustrated and somehow inadvertently I left the letter lying around.

A couple of days later I thought I was on my way to hell when my mother raised the subject. 'Who's been writing love letters, then?'

I wanted the earth to swallow me up. I turned crimson.

'What sort of son of mine would write a letter like this? We have brought you up properly and this is how you repay us?'

The tirade continued and I felt beaten into submission. It ended with some comment about not getting involved with girls until I was nineteen. Nineteen! For God's sake, I fancied them now! I was banished to my bedroom, in disgrace. What is all this life about? I asked myself. My pride had again been hammered into the ground – that is, if I had had any to begin with. My life had no meaning and I had lost all sense of direction. I was beginning to ask questions generally and kept asking myself, 'Who am I? Where did I come from?' I wondered why my real parents had given me away.

I was often in adult company and, of course, one learnt to listen carefully to their conversations. Quite often they would come out with statements which were irrelevant to them but not to me. For example, they would say, 'He gets that off his father' or 'He is just like his mother'. Sometimes, however, these were directed at me.

One day we were introduced to an acquaintance of my parents. This acquaintance greeted me warmly, saying, 'Hello John. I am pleased to meet you; you look just like your father.'

Now there was nothing wrong technically with this statement, but I knew it could not be true and my mind was in turmoil as I asked myself all the same futile questions which I had asked a thousand times before. By now one theme kept recurring: Where were they? Did they ever think about me? Of course, judging from the scant information held in the *magic* box, it was apparent that if *anyone* thought about me, it would probably be my mother, as there were no details regarding my father at all. How could I find out?

I must be doing something wrong – after all, that is what we were taught at school. More prayer and a humble disposition and the way ahead would surely reveal itself. Of course, a prerequisite for this was the one thing I was lacking in: Faith. Nevertheless I was determined to get myself on the right path and I examined my conscience, searched my soul and set about praying, earnestly.

I had a great opportunity coming up, as we were going on holiday, or should I say a pilgrimage to that holy of holy places, Lourdes. I don't know what I expected to find there, but it was not inner peace and a way forward. We travelled from Manchester to Lourdes by coach, accompanied by several priests from the Salesian order of St John Bosco. The first embarrassment I had to suffer on this trip was to have my confession heard 'face to face', instead of in the normal way, which was behind the curtain of the confessional box. I felt deeply embarrassed at having to do this; after all, I was only a child. However, the day soon arrived for me to be bathed in the 'miraculous' waters which were supposed to have special powers. Bathers had to queue to get in the water. I had only moved a few yards down the line when I was moved to tears. Crippled people, spastics, people with distorted features and human beings with all sorts of afflictions were being escorted to the bathing area, some in wheelchairs. This was not pleasant and I tried to turn my eyes away from the spectacle. But it was impossible. I reached the front of the queue and my turn was about to come. The thought of bathing in the same water as hundreds of others, in a confined space of about six feet, turned my stomach. Indeed I had already mentioned this to my parents, but to no avail. 'You will not catch any disease here; these waters are Holy,' explained my mother. The man organising the proceedings told me to strip. I felt my cheeks turn bright red and for a second I thought it was naked bathing. Then I realised I could leave my underpants on. This was better, but it was still bad enough. I was wrapped in some garment, the same garment all the previous bathers had worn. I shuddered at this thought. Some of them had skin problems – I had seen that whilst waiting in the queue. One old man had a severe form of eczema, with boils protruding from his neck, and he had only been a few yards ahead of me. I indulged in a few mumbled prayers, requesting that I be kept safe from the affliction that this man was suffering from. God, how I hoped this water was pure! Before I could step forward, the organiser asked me if I could walk. I was taken aback by this question and, almost before I could answer, I was lifted off my feet by two stewards and immersed in the cold water. This action took my breath away and I shut my eyes when I went under. It had only taken a few seconds, but I was very glad when it was over. I went back into the cubicle to dress. So now I was one of the lucky few who had benefited from the waters of Lourdes. If things were going to improve, then surely the improvements would show themselves soon, if not today, then perhaps in a few days' time. After the week in Lourdes, we were whisked off on a whirlwind tour of the major cities of France. This was not just any tour, but a tour of the famous saints and martyrs. We visited several whose names I could not remember, with the exception of the one and only St Bernadette, the saint who had caused me so much ridicule several years earlier. Now this was the saint who had seen miraculous visions. In fact the Holy Virgin herself had appeared to this saint, bringing messages from above, although it was never quite clear to me just what these messages had revealed. Anyhow, I was reliably informed that if I prayed beside her body, my requests would be granted. The first problem I had was that I asked the wrong question.

'How can a body almost a hundred years old look as good as new?'

'Don't be so silly,' I was told. 'This is the body of a saint and it will always look young.'

I had been chastised severely this time. I knelt beside the body and prayed earnestly. At the same time I knew my 'Faith' was faltering. I sincerely hoped St Bernadette was listening, and also that she was as good as she was made out to be. She wasn't, and after another week of religious pioneering we returned to England. I was more confused than ever.

I had long since thought that the education and teaching methods at my school were lacking, to say the least. The teachers were a collection of oddballs, and several of them proffered homespun philosophies on a range of topics, particularly religion. Their views were most definitely not, in any way, shape or form, connected to the standard curriculum: For example, the deputy head decided to impart his own particular views to us, on the matter of the height of Jesus. In his wisdom, he categorically informed us that Jesus had been six feet tall not an inch more nor an inch less: the perfect man! Despite the fact that most of the pupils were twelve years old, we were too scared to question this dogma, in case we were shouted at, or, even worse still, received the cane, for challenging this profound statement.

One day, another gem appeared from his coffers. 'There can be no doubt that Jesus was a miraculous conception. This has been a dogma of the Catholic teaching, since the church was founded by St Peter.' A few weeks later he came out with a contradictory statement: 'It is pretty certain that Joseph spermed Mary.' Now whatever the real story was, the Catholic church could not have it both ways. But knowing the Catholic teachings, perhaps they could. With this sort of nonsense it was no wonder I was mixed up!

For several weeks we had been listening to a radio programme on Thursday mornings, which focused marginally on biology. Marginally is the correct description, because we never actually had biology lessons. The standard subjects at this school were English Language, Mathematics, French, History and last but not least, Scripture Knowledge. This last subject was also known as Religion. A thin paper book accompanied these radio lessons, to act as a guide to the forty-five minute sessions. This was the final week and the whole class was waiting eagerly for the lesson as the topic was human reproduction. We all returned to the class after our mid-morning break, books at the ready. 'We will not be having the lesson today,' announced our teacher.

A dozen or more hands went up in dismay. 'Why not, sir?'

'Because the headmaster has decided it is unsuitable.'

Murmurings could be heard all over the room. 'Unsuitable; unsuitable for who?' A number of the males felt that it must be unsuitable for the headmaster's precious girls. This then was the sum total of my education on the subject of the facts of life.

The one good thing the Catholic religion taught us, I suppose, was persistence. With the constant repetition of the same prayers, up to four times a day, one couldn't help but be persistent. What was that phrase? 'Give me a child before the age of seven, and I will show you the man'. Therefore I made a conscious decision to pray daily to St Jude, the patron saint of hopeless cases. I would ask for guidance, with the hope that I could unravel some of my past. For someone so lacking in faith, this involved a major effort on my side. As a booster to this, there was to be a mission for two weeks at our church preached by the 'Redemptorist Fathers'. Now what exactly this meant I wasn't quite sure, but I was soon to find out. A group of sadist priests was about to invade our church and our lives. The church was packed to the rafters five nights a week for two solid weeks. The congregation had to listen to the ranting and raving of some frustrated priest informing us that almost everything we did was a sin, a mortal sin. We were reliably informed, and the devil will tell you, that there was no evil in certain pleasures, and that there is no great sin in missing mass on Sundays. But there will be no doubt about the seriousness of these things when you come to die. All your sins will come clearly before you then, for example, making bad confessions and sacrilegious communions, ignoring the corrections of your parents and superiors and deliberately dwelling on impure thoughts. In fact, no stone was left unturned, and all this was delivered by the priest with cheeks bulging, sweat pouring from his brow and forced gesticulations, for a more dramatic effect on the audience. At the end of the two weeks I was mentally drained, and if I had had any modicum of faith at all before, it had now ebbed away.

# Chapter V

## A SMALL MORALE BOOSTER

I was thirteen, diminutive, shy and lacking in self-confidence and self-esteem. Above all else, I didn't know who I was, where I had come from and where I was going. The one attribute I did have was my athleticism and some ability on a soccer field. My fitness level was second to none. I could run all day and never feel tired or breathless. Where had these skills come from, I would wonder. Had I inherited them? I could also sing and had learnt to play the guitar quite competently. All self-taught. The most recurring thought however, was always the same: Who is David O'Neill?

By now, I would quite often return to the *magic* box, extract the papers and reread the documents relating to my adoption. But I couldn't explain why. All I knew was that I was searching, but I wasn't sure what for. The name O'Neill did not mean anything to me except that it was Irish.

One day I plucked up the courage to ask my mother a question, hoping, of course, that this would lead to further information about my past. 'Where was I born, Mum?' I thought this was a clever question.

'In Prestwich, Lancashire,' was the reply, and the conversation closed.

September arrived and my grandfather passed away. Of course we had to attend the funeral. This was a depressing sight: grown people in tears by the graveside, grey clouds in the sky and the priest standing in black vestments, adding to the gloom of the situation. We returned to the house trying to comfort my grandmother and be as cheerful as we could. Strange faces appeared, greeting each other like long-lost acquaintances and then, suddenly, a sobering thought crossed my mind. These aunts, uncles and cousins were not really mine at all. They were surrogates. I immediately began wondering where, if it hadn't been for a quirk of fate, I would have been on this particular day.

My insecurity had been mounting for a while but so too had my resolve and I was determined to take *some* action, whatever it might be. I went down to the city centre of Manchester, to the central library, reference section. I had been rehearsing what to say, but I still didn't feel confident. 'Excuse me, do you have a section which traces births?'

'What sort of births?'

I was flummoxed. I hadn't expected a question back. 'Where people are born.'

'Can you be more specific?'

As usual, my cheeks started colouring. 'Oh, it's okay. I will leave it till another day.' I was secretive enough already – I wasn't going to share the nature of my enquiry with anyone. Just where I was going to find any information, I did not know. My spirits were flagging again. I could do without this.

I had long given up praying, as it was both futile and boring. St Jude, the patron saint of hopeless cases, had failed to intercede, on my behalf anyway. What I didn't know was that I was about to get another classroom grilling off Father Gannon, albeit of a different kind.

We were not well off, just a working class family living in the suburbs of Manchester. My grandfather, however, owned a furniture removal firm a few miles away and lived near the school and the church. Now Gannon wanted to build an extension, to make his church into the shape of a cross, but this would cost thousands of pounds and it would take a lot of fund-raising to achieve it. He was asking us all to attend the next fund-raising event and to get our parents to attend also. This was to be in the form of a Summer fete on the thirty-first of May. He had just finished announcing this, when he directly addressed me. 'Your grandfather is a very rich man; ask him to give me one thousand pounds for my church.' My classmates stared at me in disbelief. Red hot flushes burnt my cheeks. I could not believe what he had just said. I didn't know if my grandfather was rich – he didn't appear so. But I had been humbled, again by this very same man in very similar circumstances. It seemed to me that I was always being belittled in front of the other pupils, and the one thing which I just could not tolerate was unjustified ridicule. Occasionally, however, the wheel of fortune may spin in your direction, albeit for a short time, and for once out of the despair sprung a little hope.

Later the same evening I mentioned this latest incident to my mother. She didn't overreact. 'Tell Father Gannon to do his own dirty work.'

'Oh I couldn't do that; he is very short-tempered,' I replied. 'Sometimes he talks quickly and no one can understand him, because of his Irish accent.'

There was a pause, as if my mother was thinking. Then she continued. 'Your mother came from Ireland, Bridgett O'Neill.'

My ears pricked up, not knowing what was to come next. 'Where about from?'

'Oh we don't actually know. All your father and I know is that she was a chemist. The nuns from your convent told us.'

I was hoping for more information, but that was all my mum knew and I believed her. So now I had one minuscule piece of information, which I had not had before. The only problem was that I didn't know what to do with it. My subconscious did though, and set to work with some hard thinking. The first thought was about my mother. She was the one who had left me with the nuns. But why had she done that? I suddenly had a feeling which I had had for almost all of my life, but had never been able to put into words before. But now I could. I didn't actually like the word 'rejection'. I became angry again. No one had ever discussed with me why anyone would want to give away their new-born baby. I just could not comprehend why this could have happened. The one thing which I felt certain of, however, was that she could not have loved me. There could be no doubt about that. Then I wondered how old she had been at my birth. Perhaps she had been only fifteen or sixteen years of age. A third even more repugnant thought entered my mind. Perhaps she had been raped. I didn't want to dwell too long on these negative thoughts. I wondered about my father – perhaps he also was called David. Was he also a good footballer, like myself? Good and bad thoughts came thick and fast, until I could no longer make any sense of it all. I forced the issue out of my mind, but as usual the demons returned, to haunt the innermost recesses of my mind. I was armed with very little information. The established facts were as follows: Firstly, I had been born in Prestwich; secondly, my mother was Irish, and thirdly, she was a chemist. My mind dissected the information over and over again. Logic would suggest that my mother was living in the vicinity of Manchester – after all, I had been born in the suburbs. But she might now well be married, and her name might have changed. I was again at a dead end. Returning to the central library, I scoured the shelves, looking for any books on adoption. But it was fruitless; I could not find anything and I was still too embarrassed to ask for help. My search fell into temporary decline.

One thing I had come to notice about myself was that I was extremely sensitive in certain situations. For example, if I was unfairly criticised or wrongly accused of something, the tears would well up in my eyes uncontrollably. At the same time my anger would explode with an uncontrollable force. I used to worry about this constantly, because I did not understand what could possibly be the cause. Of course adolescents can be extremely hurtful to each other in word or deed and I did not escape venomous remarks from my schoolmates, particularly about my small stature. The only problem for me, however, if I was on the receiving end, was that I would harbour the hurt inside, as I did not appear to have an escape valve. My feelings would then turn from anger to downright hatred of the person issuing the sarcastic remarks. This I understood much later in life, was due to 'low self-esteem'. Where had I heard those words 'self-esteem', before? I had been feeling pretty sorry for myself and I couldn't see any light at the end of the tunnel. Had Providence decreed a 'raw deal' for me permanently or would there be some warm moments for me to savour, no matter how fleeting?

It was now 1961 and yes, I *was* a boy of tiny stature, but my tiny body contained the ambition of an Olympic competitor and the heart of a giant. My ambition was to become a good footballer, a very good footballer – indeed, the *best*. In the years prior to this date I had practised to the utmost, but my horizon had looked dim when I had looked around and gazed forlornly at my tall and strenuous classmates. My ambitions had taken a severe knock but

I had continued. I had had few problems being selected for the school team but, because of my size, I was always selected as reserve for the 'league' side. I had never missed attending a representative game for the league, since I had first been selected as the reserve. In 1961 I was rewarded. A player failed to turn up and, from the sideline, I was promoted into the team. I was not going to let this opportunity slip by after all this time. I did not disgrace myself. The end of the season came and went and I managed to keep my place in the representative team. I was pleased with my achievements. It was now mid-May and the season had almost been forgotten. It was 3 p.m. and the deputy headmaster and headmaster appeared and then in trooped the whole of another class. The room was brimming with bodies. The headmaster began talking and all eyes gazed upon him and a tense quietness reigned. He began to explain in detail why we were all gathered in the one room. 'It is not often, these days, that the school has something to celebrate but I am pleased to inform you all that today is an exception. The school itself has not achieved any sporting notoriety this last few years, although our teams, both girls and boys, have held their own in the respective leagues. Today, however, is of special significance for St Joseph's as we have one pupil who by example alone has placed both himself and the school on a high pedestal.' At this point a trophy appeared on his desk as if from nowhere. Those at the back of the room could not really see it clearly, as it was too far away. I was sitting halfway down a row and was not a hundred per cent clear about what the trophy represented. From where I was sitting, it looked vaguely like a netball or football trophy. The headmaster continued to explain the purpose of this award, emphasising the attributes required by those who would aspire to such dizzy heights. 'This prize is only awarded to those who are exemplary in enthusiasm, dedication, teamwork, sporting ability and sporting qualities generally.' All eyes turned to the captain of the team, as it seemed impossible that any other could possibly merit it. He moved his chair slightly in anticipation. He played regularly for the 'league' team as well as being captain of the school team. I didn't particularly like him myself, as he was prone to acting in a slightly big-headed way. Still, the prize was quite prestigious, as it was being

31

awarded by the football league committee, and on top of that he had done well. After all, it had to go to someone. The moment had arrived and the name was announced. There was utter amazed silence and I was suddenly strangled with emotion.

'Me, sir! Surely not, sir.' I was called to the front of the class. The headmaster detailed, step by step, how I had been chosen as 'Sportsman of the Year'. Then pandemonium was let loose as cheer upon cheer rent the roof. It was then that my emotion took full control of me and I burst into tears, crying uncontrollably. I just could not take this in – people were applauding *me*, and it was the strength of this applause which had brought on the tears. It was very loud indeed. I bathed in this glory. I felt as if I had reached the heights. If people cheered me, then surely they liked me! My self-esteem had been boosted, like it had never been boosted before – all in the space of ten minutes. There is nearly always a downside to every story, however, and I mentally noted that the captain never, ever came near me to say 'well done'.

# Chapter VI
## A VISIT TO THE PAST

I enjoyed my brief period of fame and poured all my efforts into becoming a better footballer. I very much wanted to become a professional. In the meantime, however, I had other matters on my mind. I was still searching. One day my parents were discussing a forthcoming garden party, to be held by the Catholic Rescue Society. I casually asked, 'What was the name of the convent you chose me from?'

'Redcliffe maternity home,' was the answer. 'You were the tiniest baby in the home and you looked so helpless, as if you needed lots of love.' So now I had a further piece of information, though this was not in written form. I intended to visit this place in the school holidays. When the holidays arrived, I scuttled down to the library to try to find some form of map for this particular area of Manchester. It was not as easy as I had thought – however, I came away with a rough street plan of the area. What was confusing me was the fact that I could not find a 'Redcliffe' maternity home in the telephone book.

I had intended to cycle there, but decided against this and took a bus into the centre of Manchester. Upon arrival I asked which bus travelled to Prestwich.

'Which part of Prestwich?'

'I am not sure,' I replied. 'The town centre will suffice.'

I arrived there not knowing where the convent was situated. Now I would have to ask all and sundry. I asked first one then another, feeling decidedly embarrassed each time I raised the question. 'Never heard of it,' was the first reply.

The second reply drove a pang into my heart: 'Where? I don't think there is any such place around here. What is it you want there, anyway? Are you sure you have got the right place?'

It felt as though I was being interrogated. I couldn't possibly tell anyone my reasons for looking for this building. I hadn't planned on anyone asking me in the first place. What now? Time was marching on. I will find the police station and ask there, I thought. And say what? I was becoming frustrated – they were bound to ask why I was going there. I couldn't have come all this way, for nothing! If I get asked, I thought, I will make up some cover story. Forty minutes expired before I found the police station. I tried to compose myself and walked boldly up to the entrance.

A tall bespectacled man stood at the desk. His thick blue policeman's jacket covered his broad powerful chest, and the sleeves pushed up beyond his elbows revealed gnarled, muscular forearms of a shade almost as dark as the tattoo marks which covered them. In his mouth was a pipe, from which blue smoke curled upwards, above where I was standing.

'What can I do for you, young man?'

'I wondered if you could tell me where Redcliffe maternity home is, please?' I asked nervously.

'Redcliffe maternity home – can't say that I know it.'

I waited for that next dreaded question. But instead, he turned to a colleague in the background. 'Redcliffe maternity home, Alf, ever heard of it?'

A man appeared in a blue uniform and I noticed that his trousers were held up by a thick leather belt. Bushy eyebrows overhung a pair of deep blue eyes, which radiated warmth – or was it pity? 'What are you looking for? Redcliffe – where?'

'It's a maternity home,' I croaked.

'Well, I have been stationed here since 1954 and the only place I can think of which fits your description closed down quite some years ago. It's now council offices. It's up on Middleton Road.'

I thought he would ask why I wanted to visit this place, but he continued. 'It's the council offices you want, is it?'

'Yes, that's the place; it used to be some sort of home, run by the nuns.'

'Well, do you know where to go from here?' With that final statement he proceeded to offer me directions.

That's all I need, I thought. It's closed down! After several false starts I eventually found my way to Middleton Road. A large imposing building was set back in its own grounds with a very long drive and beautiful landscaped gardens. I commenced walking up the long drive and, as I did so, I remembered that I had been here before. Then I had been seated in the back of a car and my parents were in the front talking. We must have been making a return visit to the convent some years after my adoption. It was standard practice in those days. It was the long sweeping drive which had triggered off this thought, but it disappeared as rapidly as it had come. As I reached the main doors, I suddenly thought, What am I doing here?

However, before I had answered my own question, my subconscious answered it for me: Although you are not going to find any information here, you are reliving some of your past. After all, it was only fourteen years ago that you were brought here, and for a short period you actually lived here. At that precise moment I remembered feeling *good* inside. I was examining the outside of the building and trying to recollect what the inside looked like when someone came out through the doors.

'Can I help you?' A tall man with horn-rimmed spectacles had asked the question.

'Yes. Excuse me, are these the council offices?'

'Do you want anything in particular?'

'No, I am meeting my mother here. I wasn't sure if this was the right place.'

'Does she work here?'

I began to get uncomfortable. Why the never-ending round of questions? 'Oh no, she has a meeting at four o'clock and I arranged to meet her here.'

'Why don't you wait inside, at reception.'

This was becoming too difficult. How would I get out of this one? If I didn't go inside he would become suspicious. 'Yes, thank you.' I moved towards the door and he watched me carefully as I did so. Inside the building was a reception desk, which was so high that it towered above me. A lady came forward, sorting out some papers as she did so. 'Can I help you?'

I felt myself trembling. I didn't want to be in this embarrassing position. 'I am waiting for my mother; she said she would meet me here.'

'What's her name?'

This latest question was too much for me. Why didn't people mind their own business? 'I think I will look outside for her,' I stammered, and with that I rushed outside and began walking down the driveway. I was halfway down the drive when a car pulled up.

A voice spoke – it was the same man whom I had met at the door. 'She has not yet arrived then?'

When was this going to end? 'No, she must be late. I am just going to the road, to keep an eye out for her.'

'She will be here soon – I am sure. Don't worry.' He drove off into the distance. It took several minutes for me to calm down and then gather my thoughts. The outside of the building I remembered, even though the memory was quite vague, but the inside I just could not recall at all. Surely this was hardly surprising. As far as I could make out, I had only been here twice – once as a tiny baby, of which I had no recollection at all, and the second time with my parents: and as I had been a mere infant on that occasion, I could not remember what the visit had been about anyway. I wasn't sure at what age meaningful memories began to stay in one's mind; nevertheless, although I hadn't learnt anything new, I felt pleased with myself for having made the effort. There was definitely one thing I was beginning to learn about myself: I most certainly did not care to share with total strangers intimate details about my past. From now on I would be extremely careful about to whom I would allow access to my innermost secrets. After all, it was no one's business but mine.

# Chapter VII

## SEEKING ADVICE

Whilst I no longer believed in the teachings of the Catholic church, I felt that they owed me something – indeed, I felt they owed me quite a lot. After all, what other poor young teenager spent his own free time knocking on doors asking, embarrassingly, for the 'Outdoor Collection'? As if the poor parishioners were not asked to contribute enough when they attended mass on Sundays, they were subjected to an intrusion of their homes on a Friday evening by me, requesting a further contribution. This would immediately go into the coffers of an already overflowing pot, to subsidise the mega-rich diocese of Salford. This weekly exercise I had not undertaken by choice – it had been forced upon me by my parents, at the request of the parish priest. Walking the streets in all kinds of weathers, knocking on doors and asking the occupants to cough up their weekly contribution, which most of them could ill afford. I hated it. Indeed, most of these poor people no longer attended church anyway – they were only Catholics by default. Maybe they had married a Catholic, or had practised the religion many years previously. Sometimes they would be out for two weeks at a time, and then I had the awful job of asking them for three weeks' money, which could be quite considerable if it was allowed to mount up. Several times I did not have the heart to ask for the arrears and returned home with only one week's money, only to incur the considerable wrath of my mother, who told me in no uncertain terms that I was not doing the job properly. It was my duty and the church expected more! This meant that the following week I had to ask for three week's money, and I would cringe inwardly as I made my harsh request. Thus this was the sad state of affairs of a very young teenager who wanted to be out with his friends, like any normal person, not patrolling the streets like a beggar. Yes, they owed me, and I would be asking for payment, albeit of a different kind.

Confession, we had been told, was a wonderful sacrament given by God. Not only could your sins be forgiven, but you could grow stronger in Christ. All Catholics were encouraged to go to their priest in times of difficulty to ask for help and guidance – after all, that was what he was there for, to guide lost souls on to the right path. I would explain my dilemma to the priest and then he would set me on the right road. I had two choices. I could speak to him alone after mass or I could enter the confessional box and explain my problem there and then. Whatever route I chose, I had the satisfaction of knowing it would all be confidential. I had nothing to lose. I chose the latter route.

Six o'clock on a Saturday evening was a good time to choose as there were not many people around at that time. I entered the box. 'Bless me, Father, for I have sinned.' This was the obligatory introduction. But then I went on to explain that I hadn't come to make a normal confession – I just wanted some advice. 'Father, I wondered if you could give me some advice on a very delicate matter. I don't really know how to broach the subject.'

'Yes certainly, my son. What is the problem?'

'Well, you may or may not know that I am adopted, and I want to know the best way to go about tracing my real parents.'

There was a pause, which told me that I wasn't going to like the bit that was coming next. 'Have you discussed this with your adopted parents?'

'Well no, I didn't want them to know, as it is a delicate matter.'

His voice went up several pitches. 'You didn't want them to know, but they have got to know! Have you taken leave of your senses? The devil has got a hold of your mind; you must make a full confession now.'

'But Father, I haven't done anything wrong! I just wanted help.'

He carried on with his tirade of abuse. 'You come into my confessional box in this state of mind – I have got to say to you, you are in a state of mortal sin. Now as you know, one mortal sin is sufficient to cast the guilty sinner into hellfire and brimstone. Who else have you told about this, and what have you been thinking?' He lowered his voice. I had in fact become concerned that people outside could hear bits of the conversation, as his voice had been booming a second or two earlier.

'Now I suggest you go outside, examine your conscience and then come back in and make a full confession. Then, as long as you have perfect contrition, and I mean *perfect* contrition, I can absolve you from your sins. Do you understand?'

'Yes, Father,' I said humbly, and with that I went back outside.

Twenty-five minutes elapsed before I summoned up the courage to re-enter the box, by which time the church was almost empty anyway. Now I was trembling with fear because the priest had told me that I was destined for hellfire, and although my beliefs were not very strong in this area, for some reason today I was genuinely frightened. 'Bless me, Father, for I have sinned,' I recommenced. 'It is eleven months since my last confession.'

Before I could go any further, he launched another attack on to my already weakening armour. 'Are you telling me you haven't been to confession for eleven months. What sort of a Catholic are you? You are heading for excommunication – don't you realise that?'

'I am sorry, Father.'

'Sorry, sorry! Being sorry is not good enough.' Then there was a pause. 'You will have to go to another priest for absolution. I cannot absolve you, as I don't feel you have perfect contrition.'

With that I rose and quietly closed the door. God help me if I had been a murderer, I thought.

'This sure is an understanding church!' I shouted, as I walked into the car park.

# Chapter VIII

## LIVING WITH REJECTION

Several years later I left school and took a job in a bank. Over the last couple of years, I had picked up snippets of information regarding the adoption process. I wasn't quite sure where I had obtained the facts, but I now knew for certain that the adoption process in Great Britain appeared to be shrouded in mystery. One absolute certainty was the fact that the laws were designed to protect the parents who gave up their child for adoption, and probably the adoptive parents also. No one seemed to have given any thought to the poor unfortunate individuals who were out there searching, either mentally or physically, for both themselves and their origins. Whatever was to happen to me in this life, I would not be deterred. I believed I had some rights, even if the law decreed I didn't.

My seventeenth birthday arrived, and although I had *some* confidence, my true extrovert nature remained hidden behind a veil of insecurity. But the immature adolescent who had first walked into the central library at thirteen years of age had now gained a lot more confidence, especially when it came to asking where to find birth records. I approached the woman behind the enquiry desk.

'Hello, could you tell me where I could find the birth records for this area?'

'I am sorry, but we don't hold records here; they are held centrally in London.'

'At the London library?'

'No, they are held at Somerset House, I think.'

'Would you have the address?'

'I think so; can you hang on a minute?' She returned a few minutes later and pointed out that it was St Catherine's House, and not Somerset House, as she had first thought.

I was slightly taken aback by this new finding, for London seemed a long way off. I had never been and I couldn't think of any legitimate excuse to make a visit. I would have to think about this one for a while. Occasionally events would happen, even though they seemed to be small insignificant events, which made me think that someone else was controlling my destiny. One such event was about to happen. Several months elapsed and I was still trying to think of a reason to visit London, as I knew I would not be allowed just to travel down on a whim. Then by a quirk of fate my employers announced a day trip to London in February. I had been out once with a girl from the bank – her name was Kathy – and I again plucked up the courage to ask if she was going too. 'Yes,' she replied.

'We will go together, then, not with the rest.'

'Yes, that's okay.'

I was incredibly pleased because she was far too good-looking for me. I could not work out why she had agreed. When the day arrived we boarded the coach early in the morning and I casually asked if there were any places she would like to visit.

'Not particularly,' she replied.

I then asked her if she would mind us going to St Catherine's House, perhaps for five minutes, just so I would know where to find it. It was obvious that it would be closed on a Sunday.

'Not at all.' She didn't bother asking me why I wanted to visit the place. We arrived in London and a couple whom we had been chatting to on the coach asked if we would like to spend the day in their company.

I was about to agree when Kathy answered for me: 'No.'

I didn't know where to hide – I felt so embarrassed. On top of that I was angry, because she hadn't consulted me. I tried to put this to the back of my mind.

'Where shall we go first?'

'I don't mind,' she replied. We spent the whole morning visiting various famous sights and then had some lunch. Early afternoon came and we had exhausted the places we wanted to visit. It seemed an appropriate time for a slight detour to the one place I wanted to visit, but she had other ideas. She steadfastly refused to go anywhere, other than back to the coach, certainly not to St Catherine's House. She was weary and wanted to rest in the bus. I was devastated by her refusal – after all, she had promised, and now she had let me down. I was figuring out if I had enough time to make the visit solo, once we arrived back at the coach, but it would have been touch and go, and we were instructed that the vehicle would leave on time. Years of pent-up emotion were rapidly turning to anger and I was unable to vent my feelings in a way which felt appropriate. The trip was over and I felt a great sadness come over me. Some relationships are bound to be more special than others for young teenagers, by their very nature, and for a while I couldn't believe how lucky I was. I was the envy of all independent observers, for she was a truly attractive girl. Of course my parents were not stuck on her at all. 'Too flirty by far,' was my mother's description, and that was bound to be the kiss of death.

I had become besotted with the girl and ferried her around in my car at her slightest whim and fancy. Beauty is in the eye of the beholder, and when passion reigns supreme then love is definitely blind. A mixture of emotions engulfed me, dazzling me so brightly that I could not see the rocky road ahead. Her parents, she informed me, would not let her go out night after night, and after a week's demanding work at the bank she liked to rest at the weekends. I was used to playing soccer on Saturdays anyway, and then meeting my football friends in the evenings.

Seeds of doubt began to root themselves in my mind when I suggested we meet one Saturday evening. She did not really offer a proper excuse for her refusal and I immediately suspected that something was amiss. I broached the subject one lunchtime, whilst we were at work. Confronting this problem proved to be very difficult, as I had suspected, but there was no way I was going to be trampled on again. Give her an inch and she would take two miles!

She stormed out of the lunch room in such a huff that she dropped her handbag on the way, scattering the contents on the floor and under the table. She picked up an assortment of miscellaneous papers which had fallen out and hastily stuffed them back in her bag, several of them falling to the ground again. She made another attempt to retrieve them and disappeared into the back room. I stood there in dismay, unsure of how to address my problem. Then I noticed something lying under the left-hand corner of the table. I picked it up. It was a letter, a letter written to Kathy. By now I was past the point of return. I started to read. It began, 'My darling Kathy,' or words of that order. I could not summon up the courage to read its contents so I turned to the second page to find out who had written it. I felt a pang through my heart. It was signed by someone named Andy. My temper was at boiling point; I had given my all to this girl and this was how I was being repaid! I tackled her about the subject and she nonchalantly admitted that he was her boyfriend. What did that make me? I remembered I had asked myself this question before, but that had been in a different light. Over the next few weeks, familiar feelings returned to haunt me, slowly but surely. It took some time for them to sink in, but once they had, there could be no mistaking them. I had been rejected again, albeit by a different woman.

# Chapter IX

# TWO OF A KIND?

It was the fourth of November, at about 6.20 p.m. I remember it as clearly as if it was yesterday. The doorbell rang and a man was standing in the dark foggy shadows. 'A telegram for John Pickersgill,' he said.

Before I could take it from him, my mother grabbed it from his grasp, thanked him and rushed into the house, tearing the document open.

'It's addressed to me,' I yelled.

'It can't be yours – who would send you a telegram?'

I felt extremely hurt by this remark, even though I hadn't got a clue about who could have sent it. After all, I had never been sent one before. I noticed that she was agitated, but I couldn't fathom why. She read out the contents, looking slightly less disturbed. 'It's from Crewe football club; they want you to attend a football trial, tomorrow evening.'

My heart lit up. I had been forewarned about this and now it was about to happen. The only problem was that I was suffering from a dreadful virus and felt particularly under the weather. Nevertheless, I arrived at Crewe on a murky damp night, got changed and played the game. I was awful. I had picked the wrong night to be off form, although some of this was down to the way I was feeling. I didn't make any excuses to myself however, as this was one situation over which I had control. I never heard another word from them. Stockport County then invited me for a similar trial, but that ended with me walking from the ground, late one Thursday evening, with tears in my eyes. I would have to accept that I was just too small, but I could not. By the mid-sixties, I had put on some weight and had grown several inches taller as well. This time I was invited to Bury, not once but three times, and on the third occasion I was asked to play for the junior team. Things had started to look up. I soon discovered, however, that one can have talent and use it to very good effect, but other factors come into play over which one has no control. That seemed to be the story of my life so far. I was certainly playing well, but the person in charge of the team now was not the person who had invited me to play in the first instance. I picked up vibes that he did not like me for some reason, and I noticed he had favourites who were doing less well but whom he would praise to the hilt. When the chop came, it came without warning, with not so much as a word, not one word. It all happened so quickly, and I was back playing with my amateur club all in the space of seven days. All of my major hopes and aspirations had been dashed without a word being spoken, and that ugly sentiment reappeared: rejection. The only difference was that this time, it had not been at the hands of a woman.

It was becoming apparent that the way certain incidents unfolded in my life could be likened to the 'Libran' scales swinging back and forth, as if to illustrate that the scales must first swing one way, then the other, before equilibrium is found. The strange thing was, I had been born under the seventh sign of the zodiac: Libra. Surely, following this latest turning point, I was due a morale booster?

I met her at the fairground, which visited our part of the world on an annual basis. Her name was Geraldine and she seemed to be quite taken with me. A mutual rapport was formed almost instantaneously. I asked if I could walk her home and she agreed. The conversation flowed like a good wine and it felt as if we had known each other for years. By the time we arrived at her gate, she was asking me about myself and also my family. I was always guarded when it came to talking about my family, and turned the conversation around to her family instead.

'Well, things are a bit different in my family. You see, my mother and father are not my real mum and dad.'

I stared in disbelief.

She very quickly noticed I had gone silent. 'What's the matter?'

'Nothing, it's just that I have never met anyone before in that position, apart from myself.'

'What, your mum and dad are not your real parents either?'

'No, I was adopted.'

The remainder of the evening flew by and it was now quite late. We arranged to meet again very soon and as I was about to make my exit, she whispered several terms of endearment in my ear. I was most definitely on a high and looked forward eagerly to our next meeting.

When the appointed day arrived, one thousand and one things were going through my mind and yet I didn't seem to know where to start. Would this be the start of a very important relationship, one where both parties would be on an equal footing, and, more importantly, would be capable of understanding each other's problems and difficulties? We met and eventually got down to the core subject – our backgrounds. I let Geraldine do all the talking.

'When they first told me I was adopted, I was about eleven. I became very angry towards them.'

'Why did you become angry?' I asked.

'I am not really sure, but they should have told me sooner. It made me feel as if I was different from everyone else.'

I smiled inwardly with some satisfaction on hearing this. I was most definitely not alone anymore. I was beginning to like this girl a lot.

'Do you ever wonder where your real parents are?' she continued.

'All the time,' I replied. Then I interrupted her flow. 'Do you ever wonder who *you* are?'

'Yes, that is the one thing which really bugs me. They adopted me when I was just a baby, and they don't really know much about my real parents.' She paused and the sentence trailed off, as if she was thinking. 'When they first told me, I got so angry with them that I told them I wanted to leave and go back to my real parents. They told me that this was not possible, and this made me even more angry, so much so that I told them I hated them.'

This remark stopped me in my tracks. I had never hated my adopted parents – quite the opposite. It was the *situation* that I hated, not knowing where I had come from, or who I actually was. I declined to comment and let her continue.

'They were really hurt by my remarks, especially my father, as

I had always been his *special* daughter. Eventually, I calmed down and I told them how very sorry I was for upsetting them and making them cry with my hurtful remarks. They forgave me and I realised that I love them a lot. And everything is now back to normal.'

This last remark made me prick up my ears, because the way it had been uttered told me that everything was not all right at all. 'Have you ever thought of trying to trace your real parents?'

'Well, the only piece of information I have is that my mother was unable to bring me up on her own, and that is why I was given up for adoption. Anyway, I have made a promise to myself and to my parents not to go looking for her. I don't want to upset them again.'

I thought for a moment about what I was going to say, as she was clearly emotional by now and I didn't want to say the wrong thing. However, I refused to compromise my principles.

'Well I am trying to trace them now. In fact, I have half-started, and as soon as I can I am going down to London.'

'Why London?'

'I am led to believe that's where the records are kept.'

'I don't think you should – you might upset your parents.' With this remark I felt a surge of anger rise inside me. I did not want someone telling me what not to do, particularly this young lady. 'I wasn't going to tell anyone, just make enquiries on my own.'

'Really, I don't think you should. Why don't you let me help you?'

'How can you help me?' My annoyance was rising and about to cascade like a giant wave landing on the beach.

'I have been in the same situation and I can help you face it all, you know, live with it.' She was now acting like a counsellor, not my girlfriend, and I could sense that an argument was about to ensue.

I would not be deterred and I made my point forcefully, saying, 'Well, I am going to search, whatever you say.' And with that comment, some of the warmth was taken away from the rest of the evening.

Five days later I was flying out of the country with my football friends for a ten-day holiday, which had been planned months ago. I met Geraldine the evening before and we went for a drink. The topic came up again.

'Have you decided whether or not to keep looking?'

'Yes, most definitely; it's important to me.'

'Are you not going to let me help you instead?'

'You can help me search, if you wish.'

'That is not what I meant.' Once again, the evening ended on a sour note.

I returned from my holiday extremely tired, as the flight had been held up for several hours, but nevertheless I made the effort to go round to Geraldine's house in the evening.

I wasn't mentally prepared for a difficult evening and I could sense immediately that something was wrong. What should have been a pleasant reunion could have turned into a battle scene, but by now I had become tired of being lectured to and for once I let my rising anger subside.

I tried to appear phlegmatic – I wasn't in the mood for arguing. A tension began to fill the air and she muttered something about me not really liking her. Soon it was obvious that it would be best if I left. I felt as if I had been let down again, and I had so wanted this relationship to work. But I never heard from her again. That itself was a strange phenomenon, and over the years I would often wonder what had became of her and whether she had taken the initiative to look for her real mother.

# Chapter X

# ALONE ON AN ISLAND

I had been making mental plans for another visit to London, but I was a teenager distracted and I hadn't quite thought of a good enough reason. After all, a Northern lad brought up in a strict family had to get permission to do almost anything. I still had to be back home by midnight at the latest, whereas all my friends were allowed to stay out as long as they desired. The bank announced that the annual trip to London would take place later in the year, this time in the summer months. I would recommence my search then. And with the determined resolve I had first acquired as a very small child, I would prove to myself that I could be successful. After all, I didn't need anyone else, because other folks always let me down. The compass of my mind had its sights set on London, but Providence had other ideas. My father was made redundant and it was a very difficult time for finding another job. Engineers with his skills were being sought by a company on the Isle of Man. He needed a job desperately; he applied and was successful. So now we, as a family, had to move lock, stock and barrel to an island in the middle of the sea. I personally didn't really have any choice. I applied for a transfer and by April I had moved. The whole scenario was traumatic, to say the least.

At nineteen, I was in for a culture shock, a different way of life and five years of purgatory on a desert island. I had left behind all my friends and I was now cut off from my imaginary lifeline, way down in the capital. I had a very difficult time adjusting. However, if there is such a thing as destiny, or any plan to this life we live, then it's fair to say that I was about to embark on another learning curve, and one which was of major significance to me, personally.

To say that some of the practices on the island (thirty-two years ago) were backward is an understatement. I had been living there all of six months when I managed to get myself in the local paper. I had been getting regular, good reports on my soccer skills, but this latest report was almost a blight on my character. I was dropping a girlfriend off at her home and parked for a few minutes outside her house. The next thing I knew was that a police car was pulling up. Out stepped a policeman, with torch in hand. He walked over to my vehicle and began to speak. 'Do you realise you have got no parking lights on?'

'I didn't know I had to have any parking lights on, officer. It's a well-lit street, so I turned them off.'

'I can see that, and I have to inform you that you are committing an offence.'

'An offence. How can it be an offence? Back on the mainland you don't have to bother, particularly if it's a well-lit road.'

His demeanour turned nasty. 'You are not on the mainland – you are on the island now, and under the road traffic act you are committing an offence.' His next statement was calculated to shock me and it did. He began to caution me and asked for my driver's particulars. I started to protest but it was to no avail. I hadn't been illegally parked – I just had no parking lights on. For god's sake, I didn't realise you had to have lights on! What sort of an island was this? Were all the inhabitants like this?

Within the space of ten days, I received a summons and a fine of seven pounds. This would teach me a lesson, and I thought that was the end of the matter. Fat chance. I was now the subject of an article in the local paper: 'Sitting in his car, with his girlfriend, in Castletown Road, John Pickersgill of... failed to display his lights', and so on and so forth. I could not believe what I was reading – this must have been some sort of petty joke. Surely the locals would not be interested in such trash! I was wrong, and they *were* interested. I began to scrutinise the other columns more carefully: 'Mrs Brenda Quirk of... was this week fined £6 for allowing her dog to foul the footpath'. Now these sentiments I firmly agreed with, but to publish this, and many other articles like it, was taking journalism too far. Then, to top it all, there was a regular column each week, as long as your arm, on who had been committing adultery with whom. It was totally irrelevant trivia, to anyone, unless you were the injured party, or connected in some way to the actual incident. The whole place appeared to be in a time warp and I had invaded it.

'Invaded' is a very apt way of describing matters, because if you were not comfortable living there, the locals could offer some very sound advice: 'Get back to the mainland.'

I naturally struggled to make any real friends in an environment which was alien to me, and I found it difficult to adapt at work as I felt like a stranger in their midst. I was always very serious about everything and took immediate offence at the slightest form of ridicule from the local staff, without even realising it. In the summer months, however, there wasn't much time for jollity, as we had to be on our toes. We would invariably be short of staff at a time when we needed them most. The bank would be packed with local customers and holidaymakers alike, and Fridays could be a nightmare. Thousands would be leaving the island and would want to withdraw cash, late, on a Friday afternoon. The queues would stretch into the street. There were no such luxuries as cashpoint machines in the late sixties.

It was mid-summer and a very hot, sticky afternoon. There were two of us on the tills struggling to keep the queues down to manageable levels. Suddenly my colleague left my side and disappeared into the manager's office. She didn't appear too well. Five minutes elapsed and people were complaining, at first to each other, about the length of the queue and the fact that there was only one cashier. Ten minutes went by and now they were complaining to me, in a very loud manner. I apologised, but to no avail. Someone at the back began swearing, 'I have a bloody boat to catch; where's the sodding manager?'

'What sort of a bank is this, a Mickey Mouse bank?'

The abuse got worse but still no one appeared from the office and we had no spare cashiers.

'Hey you at the back, get off your arse and start serving.'

'I am sorry but we only have two cashiers today,' another colleague replied.

'Two? Well, I can only see one and I am fed up with waiting. I have grown a bloody beard, I have been waiting that long.'

Some people started sniggering on hearing this remark. The whole episode was bizarre and I was at the centre of it, fighting off a torrent of abuse. I was now sweating profusely and I was apologising every forty seconds as new customers filed forward into the bank. It seemed like a lifetime, but it had only been twenty-two minutes since this scene had started. Another eight minutes elapsed and then an ambulance appeared, but for some strange reason the siren was not blaring out as normal. The manager's door opened and my colleague was ushered into the street and then into the ambulance. Some people in the queue sighed with relief, or was I imagining this? Anyhow, the complaints seemed to die down, and the manager took over the vacant till and we struggled on until closing time. The doors closed at 5.30 p.m. and all the staff waited with eager anticipation, for the manager to say something. The staff who had been working at the rear of the office had not really seen the events unfold, and could only guess at what had actually happened. I personally had formed my own opinion, although, at this point, I did not offer any comment.

'Quite an afternoon,' began the manager.

'Yes, I was taking some abuse about the length of the queue,' I replied. 'I didn't really offer them a reason – I just said we were desperately short of staff.'

He continued. 'It's difficult to know what to do in those situations, so I called for an ambulance.' His very diplomatic answer said it all.

The poor girl was pregnant – none of us had known – and she was on the point of delivering her child. When we cashed up the tills, my till was ten pounds short, and normally that would have caused me great consternation, but on this particular evening I had other things on my mind.

She lost her child, taken from her without warning. Physically, she was still in one piece, but as to her mental state of mind, who could know? Little matter that it would have been a very premature baby, the poor girl was distraught. She had lost a slender fibre of life; I hoped she could come to terms with it all. It made me think back to my first few weeks on this earth. I had been given away, by choice; this girl had had no choice – it was snatched away from her. I had not been given the best start in life, but *I* had survived. Perhaps my mother had delivered me prematurely. I tried very hard to put myself in her place, but I couldn't get my brain round it all. One cannot fathom the unfathomable. I could not understand why she would have wished to give me up for adoption. It seemed alien to my nature. But one thing I was sure of: I would not give up my search.

# Chapter XI

## REFLECTIONS

My twenty-first birthday arrived in 1968, and for some reason I felt I should have some form of party, to celebrate it. The only problem was that all my close friends lived on the mainland. So I hastily arranged for a party to be held in Stockport and invited all my old friends. In the build-up to this, I kept wondering where my natural mother was at this particular time, and of course if she was thinking about me. Then I convinced myself that she probably thought about me quite often, and not just at this special time. Conversely, I also thought that she might have been glad to get rid of me, and in that case she might never think about me, or if she did, perhaps it was in an unpleasant manner. My thoughts began to sway like a pendulum, back and forth, again and again. I began to notice that they would always finish on a negative note and I decided that if she had really wanted to find me she would have contacted me by now. Perhaps she was waiting for me to make contact. Surely a mother could not give up a child and never think about the matter again? I didn't know. I was not the mother; I was the son. But I was desperate for some answers.

The party came and went as parties do, and the time came for me to fly back to the island. As it happened, the party had been held over the weekend, and the flight back was actually on the day of my birthday. The plane left on time and I sat back in my seat, letting my subconscious take over after a nice relaxing drink. This would be the day, I told myself, that my mother would be thinking of me. She would be thinking to herself that her son, of all those years ago, would today be a grown man. What would he look like now? she would be asking herself. Would he look like me, or would he look more like his father?

She would probably be a little sad today, wishing she could have at least seen me, if not actually been with me. My thoughts rolled back and forth in the usual manner. Yes, I decided. I will make a big effort and get my search off the ground again. After all, I was now twenty-one and I could do exactly what I wanted. I wouldn't need an excuse to go to London. If I wanted to go there, I would just do so. We were halfway across the Irish sea, and about to make our descent to the island, when an officer emerged from the flight deck and walked down the aisle. I noticed he wasn't wearing a jacket and looked rather informal. He stopped two rows from my seat. I was seated in the aisle and had a full view of what was about to happen. He lifted a small square panel, which was actually located in the aisle itself, and began turning a small handle clockwise until it would turn no further. Replacing the panel, he then walked off towards the cockpit. Passengers stared at each other, one or two of them asking each other what it was all about. Several minutes later the plane lurched sideways, as if to change direction. Puzzled looks appeared on several faces. The next thing we heard was an announcement over the inter-com: 'Well, ladies and gentlemen, for those of you who witnessed that dramatic incident a few moments ago, we would now like to inform you that the undercarriage wheels did not drop down and, therefore, I had to wind them down manually. I am pleased to tell you, that the manual operation was successful and we now have the capabilities to land. Regretfully, we will have to land at Liverpool as we need to get you all on to another aeroplane, to comply with safety regulations.'

There was a mixture of tension and relief as passengers exchanged both comments and glances. To land at Liverpool airport would just be an onerous nuisance fraught with delay, I thought to myself. As the plane circled low over the airport, I could see what appeared to be coloured dots, scattered at various strategic points, both off and on the runway. I couldn't make out what they were – we were too high in the sky. As we got lower, however, it soon became clear that they were fire engines. They were all powered up with crew, ready to move. Other people had seen them and now some were beginning to panic. We hadn't been told the true facts and the authorities were preparing for a disaster! There would be no need for all the fire engines (I myself could count eight) if everything was in order. Some of the passengers began to call out to each other: 'The wheels cannot be down – we must be preparing for a crash landing, otherwise there would be no need for all these precautions.'

One person yelled at the stewardess, 'What are the real facts – why do we need all those fire engines?'

'It's just normal procedure in cases like this,' she replied.

Now I too was panicking. After all, there had to be some truth in what had been said – why all these safety measures, if everything was in order?

The man seated next to me wasn't looking too confident either, and he started to talk to me. 'What do you think; are the landing wheels down, or not?'

'Well, the captain says they are. I just don't like the fact that there are so many fire engines.' I didn't know what else to say. We were approaching the runway and I remember thinking quite clearly to myself, this could be the end. Was Providence about to terminate my short stay on this earth, on the day I became a man, on my twenty-first birthday? It all seemed so unreal. If this was about to happen, then everything would have been so futile. There would have been no point in me ever having been here. One thousand and one things passed through my mind. My search would have been in vain. But at that precise moment I wasn't thinking about that; I just didn't want to die. The plane landed safely and I immediately renewed my vows to look for and to find my mother, and then to free myself from these mental chains and get out of this tortuous prison.

# Chapter XII

## ALLY OR OBJECTOR?

The early Seventies arrived and I obtained the transfer to Liverpool which I had requested via my head office. For some strange reason I began to gain a lot more confidence, if not self-esteem. I put this down to having moved out of the family environment and to having to learn to make all my decisions myself. I also became an assistant manager.

Around this time my search recommenced with a renewed vigour, and I found both a new ally and an objector at the same time. My ally could not have been closer, for it was none other than my girlfriend, to whom I had just become engaged. She seemed to understand my plight, but that was hardly surprising as she had also been adopted, if not quite in the same manner. She had a sister of her own and then her mother had remarried, at which stage her new husband had effectively adopted the girls as his own. For me, life was beginning to look like a learning curve, a long and winding road, leading to the golden gate. I would be shown the objective and the subjective, time after time, and then left to form an opinion from the facts which had presented themselves. This seemed to happen a lot in my life, and the next few years were to prove no different.

The telephone rang. It was my girlfriend; she was agitated. 'Guess what?'

'I don't know, what?'

'My sister Barbara has traced our real father and he would like us to visit him, tomorrow. He says you can come along as well.'

'Where does he live?'

'It's only a few miles away; I will tell you later.'

I had a thousand and one questions to ask Barbara, not least of all how she had managed all this. I came off the telephone.

'You look flushed,' said the manager.

'Oh, I've just had some news which surprised me.'

'What's that?'

I didn't want to divulge anything to him, as I didn't trust him and, what was more, he was a pig of a man. But I had been caught off guard. He began to elicit bits of information from me, and then I had to submit to his careful questioning.

At the best of times, he would proffer his narrow-minded views on a whole range of subjects. Now, I was about to be bombarded with his homespun philosophy on the rights and wrongs of family life. He said, 'You should let sleeping dogs lie. No good can come from making a visit like that – believe me I know.'

How could he know anything, I thought. He is just a narrow-minded bigot!

'The girls should leave things be, as they have an adopted father. They will just open up a can of worms.'

Now I was angry, but this was the boss – I would have to be careful.

'It's something they feel they should do, and I agree with them.'

'Listen, I know all about these matters. Take my advice.'

'I know about these matters too,' I replied.

'How can you?' he retorted.

'Simple, because I am adopted also.' I thought I had delivered the stunning blow. There could be no way back for him now, but I was wrong.

'You're adopted? That makes it worse you should know better.'

'I do know better, and that's why I am going with them.'

'No, you mustn't,' he said, beginning to raise his voice. This was getting out of hand. There was a pregnant pause and I was just not prepared for what came next.

'Listen, my daughter is adopted, and I know what harm can come from all this.'

Now I fell silent, and my thoughts stopped for a second as if affected by a seizure. Inwardly I kept asking myself the same question: how could a buffoon like this be allowed to adopt anyone? The man was a complete nutcase at the best of times, and was prone to be economical with the truth. No one ever believed a thing he said, as he lived in a fantasy world, and he had been allowed to adopt a daughter! Now I was convinced that the system was 'up the shoot'. I suddenly felt as if he had intruded into my life, but I wasn't sure why. Then the penny dropped. I just didn't want him knowing that I was adopted. I had had no respect for him in the first place, but to learn now that he had been allowed to adopt someone felt like an injustice. Now I had to let him have both barrels.

'I am searching for my real mother too.'

'How can you? What about your adopted parents?'

'I don't intend telling them.'

'Why not?'

'Because I don't want to upset them and it's a private matter anyway.'

'If my daughter tried to trace *her* real parents I would be very angry and upset,' he said.

'She might not tell you.'

'Of course she would tell me – she tells me everything.'

By now, I knew I could not win this argument. 'There's no point in discussing this further, because I won't change my mind,' I continued.

He started up again. 'I cannot believe you would do such a thing – it's not natural.'

This was the final straw. This was the one thing that *was* natural. *Normal* human beings *want* to know their origins, beginnings and the traits they have inherited, and I would defy anyone to tell me different, least of all a clown like him. 'Well, we will just have to disagree,' I said, and with that I walked toward the restroom. All the way home I just could not get the subject out of my mind. How could the authorities let this type of person adopt a child? It was very difficult to imagine him looking after himself, let alone a child. Surely the powers that be must have screened him? I had been working with him for about a year and found him difficult, brusque, intolerant and totally lacking in the ability to understand the needs of others. All night long I weighed up the facts, sifting first the negative then the positive thoughts, but at the bitter end I still could not give the man the benefit of the doubt. Perhaps I would be able to at a later date.

# Chapter XIII

# THE MEETING

The road itself was narrow, only allowing one vehicle to pass along at a time, and since it was also quite busy, considerable confusion resulted. At the end of the road, and seeming to block it, was a church of ancient grey stone, with neither steeple nor tower but a tiny belfry at the top, and tall narrow windows which gave the whole building a look of foreboding. The house was next to the church and the two of us walked gingerly up the path and rang the bell. We did not know what to expect and we could almost hear the silence until it was broken by the sound of footsteps walking down the hall.

The door opened and we were greeted by a tallish man, with hair greying at the temples. 'Gillian, my love, it is so good to see you again after all this time. I hear you are well. And this must be John?'

I nodded in agreement and offered my outstretched hand, which he shook in a warm but firm manner.

We were ushered into the back living room where my girl-friend's sister Barbara was already seated. The usual pleasantries were exchanged and we were offered a drink. I let the alcohol relax me and sat back as an independent observer, to watch this latest plot unfold. The evening was convivial and I could sense that everyone was as relaxed as one could be. Various subjects were discussed, and I got the feeling that it was all leading up to the main topic: the reason for the splitting up of the parents, and why the two girls had been left with their mother, all those years ago. My fiancée had not seen this man, her natural father, for nineteen years or so, and it was a poignant moment.

He went to extraordinary lengths to explain that it had not been his fault that they had split up. It had most definitely not been his decision, nor choice, to leave the marital home and his two lovely daughters. He paused before he spoke. 'Your mother went off with someone else and still managed to maintain custody for your upbringing.' When he uttered these words, they came out slowly, as if they were spoken by a person with a great pang in his heart.

It was evident that there was a great warmth between these three people, and by the end of the evening I felt as if I had been a witness to some sort of play, which I had been privileged to watch. Indeed a feeling which I had not experienced for a long time enveloped my whole being, the feeling of déjà vu.

We made our way home but my girlfriend was strangely silent. I would let her tell me her feelings all in good time, when she was ready. Several weeks went by and nothing was discussed, until finally I knew I would have to raise the subject if I wanted to learn more. I waited for the appropriate moment and gently asked, 'Will you be seeing your real father again?'

'I don't wish to see him again, for although I know he is my father, it doesn't seem right, after all this time. The only father I have ever known is my adopted father, and I wish to leave it like that.'

I did not know what to say, for I had not expected this answer. Indeed this was contrary to my way of thinking. I had thought I knew this person well. I had thought I knew her innermost thoughts, and now I was wrong. But I secretly knew that I would not let this decision colour mine, no matter how close we were. I casually asked, 'Perhaps your sister could help explain to me the mechanics of tracing my mother?'

But my words had fallen on stony ground. 'Well, I don't think she could help. She didn't go to London to look – she knew a friend of my father's.' And with that she closed a chapter in her life never to be visited again, and another one closed in mine.

# Chapter XIV

## REVENGE NOT TAKEN

Back at the bank he didn't get round to asking the inevitable, as I had assumed he would. About three weeks elapsed before he commenced with his interrogation, although he said he was being inquisitive and that he wanted to help. Fortunately, for me, the subject was closed very quickly when I explained that my girlfriend did not want to pursue the matter any further. But as usual, he just had to have the final word.

'I predicted that no good could come of this. She has certainly done the right thing. It would serve no useful purpose to persist in seeing her father.'

I had already grown to loathe this specimen of a human being, and now I was beginning to despise him with a vengeance. The two recent incidents had only stirred up my venom to boiling point, and now I wanted to vent my poison all over him at the first opportunity. By chance such an occasion was about to present itself.

I was working in the strongroom when I noticed an unmarked envelope, lying between the leaves of a cashbook. I picked it up without thinking and extracted the contents. I thought it might be some old cash receipt as I could see blue, hand-written ink on a single sheet of paper.

'My darling, it was so good to see you again last night...' It was a love letter. Before I read the whole document I turned it over to examine the signature. I stood there in amazed silence. It was from him, to a lover. It was definitely not to his wife. I suddenly panicked in case he might walk into the room and catch me with the letter. I stuffed it in my pocket and went upstairs to the restroom.

Why on earth was it lying around, stuffed inside a book? It must have been placed there deliberately, for me to find it in that position. But why?

I could not figure this out. I took out the letter again and read the whole thing. It was relatively passionate and now I felt as though I was an intruder. I began to feel guilty for having read it, but, after all, I had been right to think it was just an innocent document. I hadn't committed premeditated theft. Now I was left with another problem. What was I going to do with it?

I stood there, thinking deeply. I thoroughly disliked this man as a person and he had wilfully intruded in my private life. He had, albeit by chance, discovered the one thing about me which I did not want him to know. I did not like people discovering my innermost secrets. I only revealed those, to those most close to me. What made this worse was the fact that he had impinged on the private life of my girlfriend also. So this was a double intrusion and, therefore, double retribution was called for. Providence had again intervened on my behalf – this time in a big way. Little did he know it, but he was now at my mercy. Life's hourglass would now ensure that I would obtain the justice I so richly deserved. But suddenly a haunting thought impregnated the recesses of my mind. I vividly remembered the day, all those years ago, when my love letter had been discovered. The feelings of embarrassment I had suffered that day, I abhorred, and I still did. To add to that, my philosophy was 'live and let live'. It entered my mind that this was some sort of test, sent to try me out. I couldn't work out just what the test was about, but I had to make a decision and I had to make it quickly.

I *could* stir up a hornet's nest here, and reap my vengeance, but that was not actually part of my make-up. Justice and fair play I understood, but premeditated acts of evil were alien to me. Then I began to wonder why I had entertained such nasty thoughts in the first place. No, quite definitely no. I would replace the letter where I had found it keep the facts to myself and say nothing to anyone. Although my anger reigned inside, I kept it in check.

As if fate was rewarding me, not long after this incident the officials at my district office moved me to another branch, where I was to meet a supporter of my cause. Perhaps this was my reward.

# Chapter XV
# LEARNING THE FACTS

My new manager was a lovely person and had been a very intelligent man until the booze and cigarettes had taken their toll on both his mind and body. His daily consumption of alcohol, to wash down the extremely strong tranquillisers he took, left him with a muddled state of mind, and effectively he was just a figurehead who took little part in the daily running of the branch. That was left to me. This little man, however, was eventually to play an important part in colouring my opinion on the one subject which was dear to my heart. But that was in the months to come, and for now I was just learning to work with him and getting to know his ways. One or two of these were not what was expected from a bank manager.

Several months previously I had got married, and at last the journey to St Catherine's House was to be made. We set off at 5.30 a.m. parked on the outskirts of London and took a tube into the capital. The underground was packed, and we were jammed like sardines in a tin. The whole journey into the city was awful. It was nine o'clock in the morning and I felt distinctly out of place dressed in my casual wear, when all the other passengers were smartly dressed for the office. How could they make this journey every day? I asked myself. Working in the South I just could not imagine: I was a Northerner, and in the North I would stay! Little did I think that within three years I would be living in southern suburbia.

We arrived at the famous building at 9.40 a.m. and I was amazed by the number of people scratching around at such an early hour. I was brimming with excitement and gazed with fascination, upon the row of volumes stacked neatly upon the shelves. It was hard to take in that so many people were doing something very similar. Everyone seemed to be jotting down notes, and I remember thinking quite clearly, they can't all be adopted – there are too many of them. Some of them must be merely looking up their family trees. I watched my fellow 'searchers' with great interest, trying at the same time not to let them know that I was watching them. Some of them were dressed in formal suits and looked very officious, and I wondered what *they* were doing there. Then all of a sudden that old feeling returned out of the blue, déjà vu, and once again I could not understand why.

I was so excited that I started off by looking in the 'deaths' ledger by mistake. Having corrected this, I went to the 'births' section, and commenced looking for the 1947 volume. I couldn't find it, half panicked and then realised that someone else was using it. He seemed to be taking an age writing down notes on a long sheet of paper. Eventually he finished and I took the volume from him, before he had replaced it properly on the shelf. I was unsure as to what information was recorded in these books and therefore I made a general scan of the pages first. At first glance the information looked scant, and it was. This was disappointment number one. I had been hoping that it would reveal much more. At last I located the page pertaining to myself, for 30 September, 1947. What now? I went over and asked an official what I should do.

'Damn,' I uttered. The information from the book had to be copied on to a form, which in turn had to be handed to a cashier with the appropriate fee. The certificate I so desperately wanted today would be posted to me in the next few days. My day was effectively ruined, and we set off back up the motorway for the long drive back to Liverpool. The only consolation I had was the fact that, at last, I had managed to order a piece of paper which was going to tell me a great deal more, about myself, and indeed my origins. Just how wrong could I be?

It took three days to arrive, and I was nervous and excited before opening it. I had subconsciously thought that this piece of paper would be my panacea. For some reason I wanted to be on my own when I opened the envelope and read the certificate, so I went upstairs into one of the bedrooms. After all these years this had to be a private ceremony!

I was devastated! I had expected so much more, but the certificate told me very little. Yes, it confirmed that I had been born in Prestwich, but I already knew that. But the biggest shock of all was that it showed my mother's address, in 1947, as London and not Manchester. There were two other pieces of information, one positive and the other starkly negative. Section five indeed confirmed that my mother was a chemist, but under the heading 'Name and surname of father' there was merely a blank. I kept asking myself, where do I go from here? I soon became angry again, and back came the negatives to fill my mind for weeks on end. It was obvious to me that I was unimportant to my mother – that was why she had given me up for adoption. Why should I bother to search? If I do find her, she will probably want nothing to do with me.

But this was the Seventies, and I had learnt, from various sources, that in the late Forties, and indeed right up to the early Sixties, society had frowned upon all women who conceived out of wedlock. Then a common thought crossed my mind: it takes two to tango.

Perhaps the birth certificate didn't tell the whole story. I did not intend to give up now, after all these years. I was made of sterner stuff, and all my life I had been single-minded. When I embarked on a task I always saw it through to the bitter end. Perhaps this was a trait I had inherited, and if it was, would it have been from my mother, or my father? There was only one way to find out. I would keep searching.

# Chapter XVI

## ANOTHER POINT OF VIEW

I had grown in stature and confidence since the move to my new branch, which in the main was down to my new manager. He let me assume full control while he took a back seat. I had the total run of the office. Having said that, no one was really sure if he was up to the demands anymore. At eleven-thirty he would disappear to the pub for his lunch and return at two o'clock. At 2.50 p.m. he would call over a junior member of staff and send him out for two cans of barley wine. Why drink water when one could drink wine, barley wine? He would then sit in his office and surreptitiously open the cans. He would cough loudly to disguise the sound of the can opening, when he pulled on the ring-pull. The whole episode was hilarious, because he frequently mistimed the false cough, against the sound of the ring-pull. The secret drinking remained an open secret! Nevertheless, I grew to like him, so much so that we were invited over to meet his wife and daughter. I will never forget the introduction.

'This is my wife and this is our adopted daughter, Mary.'

There was a lot I wanted to say, but I had to refrain until an appropriate time back at the office. It was a simple matter to bring the subject up. 'I didn't realise you had adopted Mary, only I am adopted too.'

From then on the conversation flowed like wine, and it wasn't long before we moved on to the more delicate matters surrounding the topic.

'I am actually searching for my real parents, at least my mother anyway.'

I half-expected the barrage I had received from the other clown, but he remained calm and replied, 'Well John, I hope you are successful. Remember, it can be fraught with difficulties.' As if I didn't know it! 'Are you going to tell your adopted parents?'

'Well, not at the present time. I am unsure about this point – it's a difficult one.'

'Well, only you can decide, if you should get to that stage.'

'How would you feel if your daughter told you she was going to search?' I had been brave enough to ask the question but was now nervous about receiving an answer.

'If she wanted to search, we would have no objection. We made that decision many, many years ago. Our love for her, and her love for us, is strong enough for all three of us to cope, and she knows that fact.'

I was mesmerised – this was so refreshing compared to the verbal diarrhoea I had received from the other idiot, and my heart went out to him. 'Do you know anything about the circumstances surrounding her parents?'

'Oh yes, we investigated the whole situation, and indeed we were vetted most carefully to ensure that we were suitable parents. Mary was the daughter of a single mother who came from an upper-class family. She was under great pressure from her parents, and immediate family, to have Mary adopted. Mary's mother was left to face this whole situation alone, as the father didn't want anything to do with her mother once she became pregnant.'

Now I was growing tense and I had to ask the leading question. 'Do you feel it is wrong for any mother to give up a child for adoption? Because I believe it leaves the child vulnerable.'

'Exactly what do you mean, John?'

'Well, if you are given away as a little baby, then this invokes a feeling of rejection, and it is hard to feel good about yourself from there on after. I must admit, I find it difficult to understand how a mother can give up her child, a few weeks after birth. After all, she has carried that child for nine months. But conversely, I also don't like the way society puts pressure on single mothers; they should be left to make their own decisions.'

'May I add,' he said, 'that situations are not always cut and dried. For example, a mother can have intolerable pressure from her family, or a single mother may feel she is offering the child a better opportunity in life. And in the worst possible scenario, some mothers may have been the victims of rape.'

'Well, I have to admit I have great difficulty coming to terms with it all, even though I have had a good upbringing. If I had a child of my own, I don't think I could give it away.'

And the conversation tapered off, as if it had arrived at a natural conclusion.

I thought about our heart-to-heart for several days afterwards. I half-managed to convince myself that it was difficult for *any* single mother to place her child for adoption, and I certainly didn't know the facts surrounding my case. But I came to a decision, a very significant decision. If I ever traced my mother, I would accept the facts, whatever they were. On that, I had no choice. If I managed to trace her, and she didn't want any contact, then I would demand that she tell me about my origins, and just who my father was. I felt entitled to that, as any human being would feel entitled. The only point, which needed addressing now, was just where I should make the next move.

# Chapter XVII

# ASKING FOR HELP

I assessed my situation. I was in possession of a small number of facts, which had been taken from my 'full' birth certificate. Unfortunately these facts didn't lead me anywhere. So was there any source, other than this piece of paper, which could help me move forward? There was no definite source, but there was another avenue and I would try it. I would telephone the Catholic Rescue Society, if it still existed. First, I had to travel to Manchester's central library, to locate the telephone directories for that area. I could find nothing resembling the Catholic Rescue Society, in any directory. So I extracted about fifteen numbers from the books which might vaguely fit the bill. I telephoned ten numbers and achieved nothing. I dialled the eleventh number and an Irish female voice answered, 'Missionaries of St Joseph.'

'Is the missionary run by the nuns?'

'It is indeed. Can I help you?'

'Well, I hope so, Sister.' And I slowly explained that I was trying to trace the Catholic Rescue Society.

'The Catholic Rescue Society no longer exists – it became defunct some twenty years ago. St Joseph's missionaries now do a similar function. What is it you are wanting?' continued the Irish voice.

I explained in detail that I was desirous to obtain some information, regarding an adoption.

'An adoption, whose adoption?'

Now I had to explain that it was my adoption, and I was growing nervous in case she declined to help me.

'Ah, now I understand. Well, we can't help you here. You will have to contact Mother Superior, and she is on another number. I can give you the number.'

I was growing very excited, as if I had found the key to the safe. But I had only obtained a telephone number! I dialled this new number and asked for Mother Superior.

'Mother Superior is not available at present, and she will be organising vespers later today,' answered a voice. 'You could try her in the morning.'

I resigned myself to telephoning the next day. I asked myself, why is no one ever available when your need is most urgent? But of course it was only urgent to me, and not to anyone else. The next morning I rang at 9.15 a.m.

'Mother Superior speaking.'

At last I was in luck! I explained my dilemma and she sounded genuinely concerned. 'But of course, John, you will have to put your request in writing and we will look into the matter. I have to say I can't promise anything, mind you.'

My spirits had been raised and lowered in the space of a minute. Her last comment was not what I wanted to hear. Surely they would have records somewhere? They had to have, didn't they? I despatched my letter and wondered how long it would take to obtain a reply. At first I thought it would take just less than a week – after all, it could only involve looking up some dusty records. A week elapsed, and then in my mind I set a target of two weeks. Two weeks elapsed and still there was no reply. I began to doubt that she had received my letter. I would wait another week and then give her a call. At the end of the third week I was growing desperate. Wait till the weekend, I told myself. Monday arrived. I would have to telephone.

'Is Mother Superior available, please?'

'I am sorry, but she is on a short sabbatical and will not be back for three weeks.'

I could feel the colour draining from my cheeks and I felt drained mentally and physically. I rang off as politely as I could. Why hadn't she mentioned she was going away? I wondered if someone else was dealing with my letter. I rang back to ask.

'I am sorry, but Mother Superior deals with all correspondence herself.'

I felt defeated. Could she not understand that this was vitally important to me? Seven weeks went by and then a letter dropped on the doormat. I automatically knew it was from the convent, as there was an insignia stamped on the outside of the envelope. I tentatively opened the letter, at the same time remembering the feelings I had had when I had opened the envelope containing my birth certificate. This time, however, I was much more full of eager anticipation. There had to be more information, as this had come from the authorities who had arranged my adoption. I looked at the letter. It was four short paragraphs, and three pieces of useless information. I was now totally and utterly perplexed. There had to be some mistake. There had to be more information. This was an error! I reread the letter:

> *Dear John*
>
> *I know you will be awaiting some word from me. Unfortunately, I have found very little, but have discovered you were born in Redcliffe Maternity Home in Prestwich, which is no longer in existence. You were baptised in the Servite parish and your mother, according to the records, returned to London.*
>
> *Sister Joseph, who was in the home at the time of your birth (and is still there) feels that your mother must have come to Manchester for your birth.*
>
> *This is only a fraction of information, and does not get you very far in your search but at least, perhaps, it fills in one little gap.*
>
> *If I can procure anything further, I shall be in touch with you. In the meantime, you are in my prayers. I hope that you will find peace of mind and with it good health.*
>
> *Every good wish,*
> *Yours affectionately,*
> *Mother Superior*

The last thing I wanted were prayers. What I wanted were facts, and more information. I telephoned again and, after a great deal of frustration, eventually got to speak with Mother Superior once more.

'Mother Superior, I was hoping for a lot more information, particularly concerning my mother. Could any information have been missed?'

There was something not quite right about her demeanour. I could sense it, even though this was just a telephone conversation.

She was hesitant, 'All the information we could find is there.'

'But what about my mother's address, date of birth, occupation. There must be something listed.'

'John, we have given you all we can under the adoption rules. There is only so much information we are allowed to divulge.'

'Who says so?'

'We are governed by the adoption act, which in essence is designed to protect mothers who offer their children up for adoption.'

Now I was getting angry. 'Mother Superior, in 1975 the law was changed to allow adopted children access to their birth records. Legislation was passed and this rule has been in force for two years.'

She was now skating on thin ice because she suddenly seemed unsure of herself. She was even more hesitant, but she still refused to give an inch. 'I am sorry John, but we are unable to offer you more assistance.' She stubbornly refused to concede and I had to back off, defeated. So much for a Christian way of life. The Good Samaritan certainly didn't reside in this convent! I felt sure that some facts were being withheld, but I was unable to prove it. But something was now nagging at the back of my mind. This letter referred to my baptism, and I hadn't given this a moment's thought before now. Surely a baptism would have required a witness and, generally, small babies were baptised when they were only a few weeks old. I thought about this for several days, but I didn't know why. Then suddenly it came to me like the rainbow after the storm. I cursed myself for being so stupid. Why hadn't I thought this through properly? Before receiving the sacrament of confirmation, all Catholics were required to be validly baptised, in the Catholic church. So there had to be a baptism certificate for John Pickersgill, or, more importantly, for David O'Neill! I was ecstatic, as if I had suddenly found my own pot of gold. The records for this, I guessed, would be held at my old school, or if they were not there, then certainly they would be in the parish records of the church, which was attached to the school, the very school where I had suffered such ridicule all those years ago.

# Chapter XVIII
# SLOW PROGRESS

I rang the presbytery and the housekeeper answered the call. The parish priest would be back after six o'clock I was told. I called at the prescribed time, and he stated, that if I would care to go down to the presbytery he would look up the records. Thursday evening arrived and I drove back to the school and church, which I had left some fourteen years earlier, when I had been a very young teenager. I rang the doorbell and the housekeeper led me into a large waiting room. A few minutes afterwards the parish priest entered and greeted me with the customary Irish accent and a firm handshake.

'Now, you wanted some information regarding your baptism. Well, let's have a look.' He extracted a large green book which was now showing signs of wear and tear, so much so that some of the pages were loose. 'Now, what year did you say you were confirmed, the mid-Fifties?'

I nodded in agreement and then I realised that these were the confirmation records, not the baptism records. I was unsure as to whether there would be anything meaningful contained therein. He sifted through the pages and eventually arrived at 'P'. Looking at the pages with him, I could see names from the past, also beginning with 'P'. Some of these were my old friends from days gone by, and these names immediately invoked memories, both good and bad. At last he reached Pickersgill, and sure enough there was some sort of addendum next to my name.

'Ah yes, you were not actually baptised at St Joseph's. You were baptised at St Anselm's, which was somewhere north of Manchester, in the Whitworth area, I think.'

I was disappointed and happy almost at the same time – disappointed because the entry was so short, but happy because here was another avenue for me to pursue.

'Just where is this church then, Father?' I enquired.

'Let's have a look in the diocesan directory.' With that he took out another book to look up the entry. 'John Street, Whitworth, near Rochdale.' I thanked him profusely and set off back to Liverpool. Within that space of twelve minutes I had obtained another tiny piece of information, and I was now feeling quite elated again. The weekend came, and on the Sunday I got out my road atlas to set off for the Rochdale area. Before I set off, however, I telephoned directory enquiries to obtain the number for St Anselm's church; I then called the presbytery to check that my journey was not going to be a wasted one. For once I was fortunate, and, after I had explained my case, the parish priest set a pre-arranged time for my visit, at four o'clock. I arrived on time and whilst the priest was friendly enough, he was strangely distant. Perhaps he thought I was odd, wanting to look up my baptismal records after all these years, or maybe he had never had such a request before. He produced an old green battered book and asked me what year I had been born in.

'1947, Father, September.'

'Now, let's see.' He ran his thumb down the columns. 'What was your original name again, O'Neill?'

I was half-expecting him to say that nothing was listed as there was a long silence, and yet it could only have been seconds.

'Here we are, David O'Neill. Baptised 19 October, 1947.' He continued, and I stood there in amazement when he next spoke. 'It's all written in Latin, but the ceremony was witnessed by Bridget O'Neill and a Kathleen Cunningham.'

'Would you be kind enough to write it all down please, Father?'

'Yes, no problem,' and with that he took out a notepad and copied the information from the green book and then handed me the paper. I was just about to turn away when I noticed an anomaly.

'I am sorry, Father, could I just check something with you? How is Bridget spelt in your book?'

He returned to the page and we scrutinised the entry together. I cursed inwardly to myself. It might not be a problem right now, I thought, but it might be a big problem later. The spelling of

Bridget was different in his book from that on my full birth certificate. The entry in the book contained one 'T', whilst on my certificate it was spelt with two. I was just about to leave when one of those thoughts entered my head. 'Father could I just take a look round the church and see where I was baptised?'

'Certainly,' he said, and he led me through the side door and thus into the interior of the church. It smelled as most churches do, of burnt incense, and the interior looked dark and foreboding. I looked for the font, which was at the back of the church, and deliberately stood in silence, trying to picture the scene: the priest was dressed in his cassock and my mother was on one side and Kathleen Cunningham on the other. The priest was reciting the standard baptismal script and my mother was answering on my behalf, 'I do, I do believe,' and whatever else was the prescribed response at that time. Perhaps I was crying when the water touched my face, perhaps my mother was crying, a last parting moment before I was returned to the convent. I had to shake myself out of this mood, for the tears were beginning to trickle down my cheeks and I didn't want the priest to see this. I thought to myself, well, John, you have been in this place before, although you don't actually remember it. And with that I took my thoughts and imaginings outside, into the rain, thanked the priest and set off towards home. So my baptismal certificate had yielded another piece of information; it referred to a Kathleen Cunningham as a witness. I wondered just who this person was – perhaps she was a friend of my mother. Unfortunately there was not a lot I could do with this information, and I was still smarting from the stubborn stance that Mother Superior had taken. If she was not going to be an ally, then I would find someone else who would be.

I had managed to procure my full birth certificate, but the new 1975 law also entitled people like myself access to a counsellor, who would: give adopted people information about their adoption, help adopted people understand some of the possible effects of their enquiries and tell adopted people about some of the complex regulations and procedures concerning adoption.

This seemed too good an opportunity to miss, as I wanted as much information as possible. I wrote to the social services department of the local authority and a meeting was arranged with the counsellor at her offices. There had to be a light at the end of the tunnel, I felt sure, and, after all, I was to have access to the experience of a trained 'counsellor'. I was literally brimming with confidence and optimism on the morning of the appointment. After about seven minutes into the meeting, however, I could feel the confidence draining out of me. She informed me that I could have access to my full birth records. I pointed out that I already had that information.

'Can I not have any information relating to the circumstances which surrounded my adoption?'

'I am sorry, but that is not available.'

'I was under the impression that the new act allowed all adopted people more information about their adoption.'

'It only allows what I mentioned to you a few moments ago.'

'I must have misread the leaflet then,' I replied. The meeting deteriorated rapidly and I was beginning to think to myself that the situation could not get any worse, when the woman began to treat me as if I was a schoolchild, with no understanding of the complications of life.

She continued, 'I am also obliged to inform you of the possible negative effects of any enquiries which you make. For example, should you eventually trace your mother have you stopped to consider that she may not wish to have any contact with you?'

I felt the anger well up inside me. 'Of course I have,' was my indignant reply.

'Quite often adopted children trace their real parents, only to find sadness at the end of the search.' This was becoming too much – she didn't have to repeat her point. But then she continued. 'In any event, you would be best not pursuing the case yourself; it would be more sensible to use an intermediary.'

'An intermediary?'

'Yes, a trained counsellor in that specific area.'

'What would be their function? Would they help me with the search?'

'Oh no, we don't have that facility available. But if you managed to trace your natural mother, they could possibly write a letter to her, on your behalf.'

'So you actually have people trained specifically for such

cases?'

'Well, they are not actually trained to deal with adoption cases, but we do have staff who deal with delicate situations, in most areas of social work. I am sure we could find a suitable counsellor within our ranks.'

I had now had enough. This meeting, which had promised so much, had been a complete waste of time, both hers and mine. The whole tone of this interview was negative, very negative. I had met resistance from the authorities at the convent, and now the social services were being obstructive. The law may have changed, but to claim that this was a major step forward for adopted people was tantamount to a lie. In the past, any person allowing their child to be given up for adoption had been led to believe that the children being adopted would never be able to find out their original names or the names of their parents. This relatively new law had been dressed up to suggest that adopted children had the right to know all about their past. But in reality, adoptees were only being offered the crumbs from the rich man's table, or, to put it another way, a few scraps of information which could have been procured anyway, by visiting London. It seemed to me that the whole world was against me finding out about my origins, something that the majority of the population enjoyed as a matter of course.

# Chapter XIX
# POSSIBILITIES

I was well and truly struggling. Without some concrete details about my mother, such as her date of birth or her married name, that is assuming she was married, I could move no further. I tried to work out how I could progress next. Logic told me that if she had married, her marriage certificate would contain information, such as an occupation, and of course, an address. I had given some thought to the fact that she could of course have remained at the address in London, which was given on my birth certificate. But my mind always dismissed this as not being even remotely likely. I would have to go back to London and order some marriage certificates. This would be like looking for a needle in a haystack, but I would give it a go.

The thirtieth of September, my birthday, was an appropriate day to return, and this time I took a train. I sat back and reflected in the same way I had done on the flight back to the Isle of Man, nine years earlier. I was now thirty, and I wondered how old my mother would be, and what she would look like. For some reason, I had always thought that she had been very young when she had given birth to me. I arrived at St Catherine's House. It was ten o'clock in the morning. I already had my plan of action and I headed straight for the marriage records. I would examine all the marriage entries for Bridgett O'Neill between the years 1947 and 1960, discard any which looked unlikely and then order the certificates for those remaining. I hoped I would not be left with too many. Three hours later I was left with nine and I ordered the marriage certificates for these entries, cringing when I had to write out the cheque for nearly thirty pounds. This search did not come cheaply! As usual, these documents were sent in the post. When they arrived, I meticulously scrutinised them time after time for any clues, hoping I could unravel the mystery I was bound up in.

There were three which I felt might be *possibilities*, but I was determined to leave myself with one. Green and black print stared up at me from the one certificate which seemed to contain a ray of hope. Four items of information looked very promising. First, this document had the correct spelling of my mother's Christian name. Secondly, the address was *London* W14. Thirdly, the year of marriage was 1960 and, finally, the lady named was aged twenty-nine, at the date of marriage. If the person named on this certificate really was my mother, then she would have been sixteen at the time of my birth. I was feeling optimistic again. The marriage had been solemnised by the rights of the Catholic church in the royal borough of Kensington and, assuming the bride had taken her husband's name, I was now looking for a lady named Bridgett McGowan. Judging from the marriage certificate, the bride and bridegroom had resided at different addresses at the time of the marriage, although not too far apart. I racked my brains, hoping a way forward would come to light. Within a minute I had a vague plan of what the next step would be. I would visit the main library again and look up the telephone directory for these two specific parts of west London. It was a long shot, but if I could find a listing for a Mr A McGowan, I could then take steps to look up the voters' roll for the said A McGowan, and Mrs B McGowan. I spent a whole morning in the library and at the end of my session I had listings for thirteen A McGowans in one particular part of west London. This was going to be a long haul as I would now have to go down to London again, to find the voters' roll, assuming they were actually on the roll in the first instance. I shuddered to think of the hassle I would be landed with if none of the people on my list were the correct people. For all I knew, they could have moved to Timbuktu. I took a day's holiday and sauntered down to London, W14 to be precise, and then encountered my first problem. I had wrongly assumed that all thirteen on my list would be on the same voters register. No such luck. I could find only seven, and none remotely resembled what I was searching for. I turned to the librarian.

'Some of the addresses on your list will be covered by three or more libraries, particularly as there have recently been several boundary changes. Do you have a car, as the first two are several miles away and the third is eight miles from here?'

'No, I came on the train and then took a tube.' I was running out of time and I hadn't thought about these pitfalls – I had been two hundred miles away, in the North.

'You will be able to take the underground to one, but then you will have a fifteen-minute walk.'

'Thank you for the map and your help.' I set off for my next port of call. By the time I had reached the second destination, it was mid-afternoon. The first entry had yielded nothing but the second one did and, eureka, there before me was the entry I so desperately wanted to see. A Mr A McGowan listed together with Mrs Bridgett McGowan! I was elated, but I suddenly realised that I still had four others to investigate. Well you have not got time today, John, so be satisfied with what you have found. If necessary, you can always come back again. I kept repeating this to myself for I had well and truly run out of time. This had been a long shot indeed, but by the time I reached Liverpool I had convinced myself that there was a very good chance that this lady could be my mother.

The only problem now was how to approach this delicate matter. A letter, a telephone call? But a telephone call to whom, and under what pretext? Without doubt this was one of the trickiest problems I had ever had to deal with.

# Chapter XX

## CONTINUED FRUSTRATION

I first decided I would write a letter to this lady, phrasing it very sensitively but at the same time explaining how I had struggled, all my life, to come to terms with my situation. If this was my mother, I was hoping she would show some understanding towards me and adopt a positive attitude.

Then I thought about the telephone, but this option appeared fraught with complications. Anyone could answer the telephone, and then just how would I explain who I was and what I wanted? Then I remembered the tense meeting with my counsellor. She had mentioned that it would make sense to use the social services, but I didn't have very much faith in what she had said to me. One thing was for sure – I did not want to mess the whole thing up now that I had reached this vital stage. I made my decision: I would go through what was supposed to be the correct channel, although this was against my better judgement. I telephoned her and hastily set up a second meeting.

I entered the meeting with positive, if not optimistic, thoughts. I explained that since our previous meeting I had done some careful research and was now willing to take her advice and enlist the aid of one of her colleagues, as per her suggestion.

'I am pretty sure I have managed to trace my mother.' I detailed step by step how I had achieved my goal, feeling quite proud of myself. She didn't reply for a second or two but merely looked at me with disdain.

'Well, I am sorry, social services are unable to help you. We couldn't possibly contact someone, unless we knew for certain that they were the correct person you were trying to contact.'

Now I was well and truly stupefied. 'I don't understand. You told me last time that there were trained counsellors to deal with delicate situations.'

'Yes, but I said that if you managed to trace your mother, we could write a letter on your behalf. You can't be certain at this stage that this lady is your mother.'

'Not absolutely, no, but there is a very good chance; I have been very thorough,' I continued. 'How can I possibly move forward without someone making contact? The only other way is for me to telephone and that is a bit risky.'

'If this person is not your mother, she may well get angry with us, as we will have intruded in her life, and we can't risk any repercussions for the social services.'

I now started to raise my voice, and there was a hint of sarcasm in my tone. 'I thought social services were designed to help the general public, not hinder them? There seems to be a rule for one but not for the other. Criminals receive help to stop them reoffending: I am not a criminal, but there is no help available for the likes of me. Why?'

'I am sorry, but that is the way it stands at present. If you are sure it is your mother, then we will be able to assist you. Until then, we can't help you.'

I got up to leave and then she came out with the standard text. 'Please contact us if you make further progress.' This was just another nail in the coffin, and I walked away feeling devastated.

'Why do I have to put up with all this rubbish. The whole bloody world is against me.' I repeated these words subconsciously before yelling them out loud, oblivious to any passers-by. Three days elapsed and then three weeks, and then Providence sent me another of those ideas, to which I attached a ray of hope, just as I had always done. This time I had an idea which would intrude on no one, and yet might still yield the dividend I sought.

I decided to place an advert in a local west London newspaper, hoping first to gain the approval of the social services. I put this idea to them and this time had a meeting with a different person, a team leader. We agreed on the following format:

David O'Neill, born 30.09.47, wishes to trace his mother, Bridgett. Write to Social Services Department, Lincoln House, St Helens, Merseyside. Reference E-CVS. If unwilling to reveal address, please give address of nearest Social Services office, where messages may be collected, or suggest alternative.

This was another shot in the dark, but I figured that about ninety-four per cent of the adult population were likely to read the local press. Just how I had arrived at that figure I wasn't sure. I made enquiries and placed the advert in the local gazette on 21 November, 1977. The trauma I had been going through made me feel like a prisoner, and I was hoping that this small advertisement in the newspaper would help set me free. I suffered all the agonies that a prisoner would suffer. First I started off with hope, the general feeling of which lasted about ten days. I assumed that anyone reading the note would think about what action to take for several days, or maybe even for a week. When, after ten days, I had heard nothing, this feeling disappeared and was then replaced by anguish. Two more weeks elapsed and then I set another target for a reply, 21 December, hoping that Christmas would come early. I then convinced myself that any reply would now be caught up with the Christmas mail, and I extended my date to 31 December. Nothing arrived, and as a prisoner locked away in a dungeon would do, I then turned to despair.

Why was I being denied this simple thing called knowledge? Knowledge of how I came to be on this earth, knowledge of my origins. Were these simple facts too much to ask for? I was learning to live with this feeling of despair, so much so that, all to easily, it had become my soul mate. I was starting to resign myself to the fact that I was destined never to find my origins, my mother and, ultimately, my real self. Weeks turned into months and still the postman never called at my door.

# Chapter XXI

## A VERY BRAVE DECISION

I had suffered so many knock-backs and rejections that I had become totally self-reliant. If you wanted to achieve success, then you did not rely on others to help you – that was my fundamental rule. I had learnt to be the master of my own destiny, and the recent events in my life had only served to reinforce this belief. However, I found it ironic that as master of my own destiny I had no control over the one issue which had haunted me for all these years. But I had become resilient and determined to triumph over adversity. I had to admit to myself, however, that I was in a dilemma and did not know what my next move was going to be.

I thought about the matter for several months, weighing up the pros and cons and, always, I came to the same conclusion. I had two choices: I could write or I could telephone. It was now April and I decided that it was time I started thinking about *my* needs and not the needs of others. All my life I had carried this weight around on my shoulders and it was time to unload it. The authorities, I felt, were totally against me, despite their statements to the contrary, and, in any case, my mother could be out there, somewhere, hoping I would take the trouble to find her. I had made a gargantuan effort so far and it would be sheer folly to give up at this stage. I had always known that the road would not be paved with gold, and I also knew that, at some time, the 'crunch' would come. That time had now arrived, and a confrontation was on the horizon in one form or another. There could be no backing off. The thirst for knowledge and truth had, so far, been a long, rocky road, but I had expected that. Yes, I told myself, I will make that telephone call. After that I would then come away with an answer, and I hoped, my misery would end. I questioned the wisdom of this and convinced myself that, at the very most, the initial call would only last ten minutes. Ten minutes, what is ten minutes out of a lifetime? Nothing, absolutely nothing, I told myself, and with that I began to rehearse my opening gambit: 'Good afternoon, my name is John Pickersgill, and I wondered if I could speak to...'

I couldn't get past the first sentence, and if I couldn't do that, how was I going to engage in this, the most delicate of conversations? The trouble with this opening line was as follows. If my mother answered the telephone, she might know who John Pickersgill was, and then possibly end the conversation there and then. If someone else answered, they might ask what the call was about, and I just could not afford to risk that. I would have to have a different plan of action, and with that I set about rehearsing a proper cover story.

I decided I would be a representative of social services, acting on behalf of someone in the community, which was actually true. It was just that the person I was acting on behalf of happened to be me! There was no other way round this quandary, and no one had actually said that I *couldn't* make the call myself. I wrote myself a script and practised daily until I no longer needed to refer to notes. I learned to say the words as professionally as I could, in order that I might sound detached from the subject matter, just as a third party would sound. I also learned to vary the pitch and tone of my voice and taught myself to pause and listen carefully, imagining a voice at the other end of the line asking all sorts of tricky questions. I wrote down a whole host of awkward scenarios, to prepare myself for every eventuality and at the end of three weeks I decided that I was as ready as I ever would be. Now I just had to pick a time and a day and get the deed over and done with.

It was a Thursday afternoon and I entered the empty manager's office and closed the door. I picked up the receiver and began to dial, but stopped before I had dialled the full number. I was trembling.

'My God this is going to be difficult,' I whispered to myself. I tried a second time and failed again. I started talking to myself to give myself encouragement.

'You only have to make this call once. You are not committing a murder, just making a telephone call, to obtain some information about yourself. People make calls all day long, to obtain information – it's just that this information is rather delicate. Now get a hold of yourself and let's make this call.'

I rang the number again and it engaged almost instantaneously. It continued to ring. After about ten seconds it was still ringing and I suddenly felt more relaxed, as if I was making an everyday call. It was just that the occupants were not at home. For some reason this gave me more confidence, or was it the fact that I had not yet heard the voice at the other end? Probably. I decided to try again later, after four o'clock. I waited until 4.50 p.m. This time I dialled without hesitation and it commenced ringing again. After about seven rings a female voice answered.

'937 4778.'

'Good afternoon, would it be possible to speak to Mrs B McGowan?'

'Speaking, who is that?'

'Mrs McGowan, I am sorry to trouble you. I am speaking on behalf of the social services department in Liverpool, and we wondered if you might be able to help us.'

'Social services department – what's this all about?'

'Well, we are acting on behalf of someone in the community who is trying to trace a relation, and this person feels that you may be able to help.'

'How can I help? I don't know anyone in Liverpool.' The voice was beginning to sound indignant. 'Who is this person and what are you doing calling this number?'

'Well, could I just explain a little further? It will only take a minute?'

'I find this most suspicious, and it is not convenient.'

'Well, the nature of the enquiry concerns someone who was born a long time ago.'

'I beg your pardon, get off this line or I will call the police.'

I hadn't been prepared for that one, and I had no answer in my script. I was getting panicky and I had no choice but to comply with her request. I put down the receiver and sat there stunned by the whole event. I was bewildered by her response. Had I struck a chord? The recipient of my call had responded with a very peculiar telephone manner, as if hiding something. And to make matters worse, the experience had been stressful and unpleasant, if not for her then most certainly for me. I tried to put myself in her place by imagining how I might have reacted, but no matter how I tried, I just could not see myself responding in that manner, unless I was hiding something. I sat there thinking intensely about what I should do next. I couldn't bring myself to phone back again in case I received another rejection, so I gave up my efforts for the day and went home. As usual, I thought about the situation for about a week, hoping I would receive inspiration. As fate would have it, another idea sprang into my mind. I would endeavour to enlist the aid of the church, the Catholic church.

# Chapter XXII

# CAN YOU HELP ME, FATHER?

I decided I would trace and enlist the aid of the parish priest, in the area where this lady lived. This would be another of my long shots, but as I had tried so many in the past, they were becoming commonplace to me now. All this, of course, was assuming that Mrs McGowan was a good law-abiding Catholic, who went to church regularly. Before I contacted the church, however, I decided to 'make a visit' to the house where this lady resided. I would not actually call at the house – I would just view it from a distance. What the object of the exercise was, I wasn't totally sure.

As it happened, this was about the time that I was moving to the south of England with my work, and a journey to Surrey was about to ensue which would give me the chance to stop off in West London, to continue my search. I planned to be in London over a weekend, so as to give myself plenty of time. I was about half a mile away from the house when I could feel the tension mounting. I gripped the steering wheel tightly. The road on which this lady resided was long, very long – I could see that from the numbers on the houses. I stopped my car and observed the numbering on both sides of the road. Yes, it was the normal odd and even numbering, the house nearest to me being number 874. I wanted 47, which was obviously about two miles further on. I sneaked down the road at a very slow pace. Someone hooted a car horn at me because I was driving so slowly. What they did not realise was that this was a traumatic time for me. What if I parked outside her house and someone came out? It felt as if the whole world was staring at me. The numbers went down slowly: 61, 59, 57. Then I parked the car on the opposite side of the road, some distance away from the house. I sat there waiting and waiting, but waiting for what? I had come to suss out the church and here I was sitting outside a row of houses, hoping that someone, anyone, would enter or leave the house, in order that I might catch a glimpse of them, and wondering if they would look a little like me. I sat for half an hour. Nothing happened. I began to feel absurd, and wondered if the neighbours were looking at this strange person sitting in his car, intently staring at number 47. I examined the house and for some reason compared it with my own. Then I reproached myself for doing this. Forty minutes expired, and then the inevitable hour. I would have to make a move soon – this was becoming ridiculous. Dark clouds appeared and the rain began to tumble. A deep feeling of sadness began to writhe in my mind. It was time to go, but I would return, I hoped in happier circumstances, in the not-too-distant future. I stopped at the first telephone kiosk and looked up the entries relating to the Catholic churches in the local area: I found three. I jotted down the telephone numbers and continued my journey south. At the first available opportunity I telephoned the first church listed, which was Our Lady of Sorrows, and asked for the name of the parish priest.

'Father Murphy will not be back until later this evening. Can you call then?'

I continued to my destination and rang at 9.30 p.m. 'Could I speak with Father Murphy please?'

'This is Father Murphy. How can I help you?'

'Good evening, Father. My name is John Pickersgill, and I am trying to contact someone who I believe is a parishioner of yours.'

'Who is it you are trying to contact?'

'I am trying to contact a lady, a certain Mrs Bridgett McGowan, and I believe she may attend your church.'

'Ah yes, Bridgett does indeed attend this church, a good lady too. What would you be wanting with her?'

I had been dreading this question, and I intended to deflect the conversation away. 'Well Father, I believe this lady may be a long-lost relation of mine, and as the situation is somewhat delicate, would you mind if I drop you a line explaining it all in writing? Then I will give you a call early next week.'

'That's all right by me; what was your name again, John?'

'Pickersgill, Father. John Pickersgill.'

'All right, John. I will expect your letter soon.'

And with that we ended the conversation. I wrote my letter of supplication explaining the situation as concisely and delicately as was possible. I let a period of five days elapse in order that he could peruse my letter carefully. On the sixth day I rang again.

'Father, this is John Pickersgill speaking. Did you receive my letter?'

'I did indeed John, and a sad state of affairs it is.'

'As you will have read from my letter, I was rather hoping you might be able to speak to this lady on my behalf, sort of intercede for me. It is a tricky situation, and I thought it one where the church would be best placed to help.'

I felt rather pleased with this last statement, as I thought I was manoeuvring him down the route I wanted him to take. But he recoiled by answering, 'I am sorry, John, I couldn't possibly do that. The circumstances are too fragile. If I spoke with her it could cause a lot of problems. For example, it would be a shock to her system, and have you considered that she may not have told her husband? We could be opening a can of worms: I am sorry, I can't be of more assistance.'

I could now feel a gloomy feeling taking possession of me again, but I persevered. 'But I had thought you could speak in total confidence with her. After all, you are used to speaking to people in confidence.'

'No John, I couldn't place myself in such a position as, ultimately, it would reflect on the church itself. You will have to find another solution.' And with that the conversation came to an awkward end. Rage succeeded my feeling of gloom and I began to utter blasphemies that would have made the 'devil' himself recoil with horror. I lashed out furiously at the nearest piece of furniture, and the least little thing began to annoy me. I conjured up the most horrible tortures I could imagine for all of the people who had refused to help me over the years. I was once again letting myself become ensnared in this state of mental anguish, and my sorrows and sufferings, with their train of gloomy spectres, were beginning to entangle me in a quagmire, which was about to swallow me if I let it. I went up to the bedroom and then all my emotion burst forth: I cast myself on the bed weeping bitterly, and asked myself what had I done that I was thus being punished.

# Chapter XXIII

# ANOTHER VIEW ON LIFE

I had to find a means of restoring lucidity and clearness of mind for I was truly in a dismal state. Those in whom I had placed my trust had let me down badly. Although I no longer practised as a Catholic, I had expected more from the convent and the church – after all, they preached the message of the Good Samaritan: it appeared that they had some difficulty in putting it into practice. By July 1979 I was residing fully in the Southern counties, and trips to my district office in London were quite frequent and not too far from St Catherine's House.

On the days when I finished my work early I would spend hours pouring through the volumes in the births section checking and rechecking to ensure I had missed nothing. When this exercise was exhausted, I moved on into the marriage section and 'bought' up a whole collection of certificates of marriages between 1947 and 1957. The operation was becoming decidedly expensive because, to date (it was now September, 1979), I had purchased over sixty different certificates, but none of them revealed any clues to help complete the jigsaw puzzle. The same melancholy thoughts would envelop my whole being from time to time. If my mother really wanted to contact me, she would have done so by now, and therefore my importance to her was insignificant. Of course I had no evidence to support this argument. She may well have wanted to contact me, but she may have felt restricted by the rules and regulations surrounding adoption cases. After all, when I had been placed for adoption, she had been informed that once the order was signed, then that was final.

Occasionally close friends who knew of my plight would proffer their own opinions by saying something stupid such as, 'You can rest assured that it would not have been easy for your mother.' How on earth could they know? They themselves hadn't any experience in these matters, and why did they never think of the suffering *I* was enduring? Yes, human beings have a great propensity for making judgements about their fellow men without having sufficient knowledge about the subject they are pronouncing judgement on. One thing was for certain: I felt I was the injured party, and on that subject I was not prepared to change my stance. As a breed, humans have the ability to behave like a race of crocodiles when it suits them, and I was about to witness this first-hand.

My final few weeks of training before being appointed as a manager in my own right, involved me working at a very large office with thirty-odd staff. The acting manager suggested I participate in, at least by observing, an interview he was about to conduct with a young female who had been missing from the office for a couple of days, apparently reporting to be sick. He felt there was more to this than met the eye and wanted to get to the bottom of the matter, once and for all.

The young woman was aged about twenty-three years, and she looked as white as the blouse she was wearing. I fancied this was going to be a difficult time for her, to say the least. The examination began.

'Lynn, you reported sick again last week, with the same ailment that you had two weeks ago. Have you been to your doctor? Only we don't want this to be a regular occurrence, do we?' I gazed at this poor woman with her ingenuous and open countenance.

'No, I haven't been to the doctor yet – I was hoping it would clear up on its own.'

'Exactly what are these symptoms which cause you to suffer with nausea so often?'

The young girl was astonished by this question and she started like a soldier who feels the blow levelled at him over the armour he wears. She was beginning to feel threatened.

'I think you are covering up the true facts, as this is the third time in as many weeks. Exactly *what* is the problem?'

This blow was delivered with ostentatious vulgarity and had a stunning effect on the poor girl in front of me. She coloured and started to grow agitated. I was rapidly forming a dislike for the interrogator and his inhumane methods.

'I can't talk about it; it is a personal matter,' she continued.

'Well, if you can't talk about it, I shall have no choice but to refer it to the district office.'

Tears began to trickle down her fair cheeks and she struggled to speak as if struck with a paroxysm of fear. There was a stony silence and one could almost feel the tension in the air. After a while she spoke.

'Is this conversation strictly confidential?'

'Obviously it depends on what you are going to say, because normally I have to report everything to the district manager.' There was no limit to this man's arrogance and lack of understanding, and I had taken a severe dislike to him.

'I would like to keep this truly confidential, if that is possible. After all, I don't actually work for the district manager – I work at this office.'

The interrogator appeared uneasy but yielded somewhat and agreed to her request.

'Well all right, on this occasion, but let me have all the facts.' There was something in his voice which I didn't quite trust – it was the way he delivered his words.

'We will keep this conversation just between the three of us?'

'Yes that will be all right.'

And with his statement the girl commenced. She struggled to start as if consumed with grief and despair. Tears were forming in her eyes again and she became even paler. She was strangled with emotion when the words came out. 'I became pregnant a while ago and last week I had an abortion.' She wiped away some tears and perspiration from her brow and waited for a comment from her inquisitor.

'I see. So that is what this is all about.' How insensitive could this man get?

'Well, I presume you are all right now, and if that's the case, you won't be having any more time off.'

She hadn't regained her composure but managed a few stifled words. 'I am all right now – I won't be having any further time off. But can you assure me that this will remain confidential?'

'Yes, I gave you my promise. Go and sit in the restroom for a while, if that will help.'

The girl left the room and I sat there mesmerised by the events I had just witnessed. Had a thunderbolt fallen at my feet, or hell opened a yawning gulf before me, I could not have been more transfixed with horror by the spectacle, which had just taken place.

'Have to be firm with these staff, you know. You will have to learn to handle problems like this from time to time.' And with that he asked me if I had any comment to make.

It felt as if my brain was bursting, and I knew I needed to meditate on my own, but that would have to wait. 'No, I don't think there is anything to add.' The words came out in an almost inarticulate voice, because I was lying. I went away to think about it. The fiend was in his mid-thirties, old enough to be ambitious, but he had acquired a hardened heart with no compassion or feeling and had trampled on, and humiliated, a fellow human being, one who was frail to start with, in order to raise himself in status. The whole incident set my mind racing, and during my hours of thought I reinforced my fearful resolution and bound myself to its fulfilment by a solemn oath. Twice in my life, fate had shown me two different instances of a tiny life being extinguished at the drop of a hat. The first lady concerned had had no choice in the matter. The second lady, however, had had two choices. Her first had been to see her pregnancy through, and produce a child (and with this thought I pictured myself, a few days old, in the arms of my mother). Her second choice had been to eliminate life at a stroke, perhaps because it did not suit her or her partner. For the first time in my life that I could remember, the emphasis began to shift, in some small way, in favour of my mother. For once all my thoughts were focused on one new fact: she also could have terminated her pregnancy, but instead she had chosen to let me live. Secondary thoughts now began to emerge. She could have left me on a doorstep for me to become one of those 'foundlings' which I had first heard about all those years ago at school. I was an angry young man and my anger was rising, but deep down I didn't want to be angry or bitter. I just wanted to know, to understand, what desperation had driven her to give away her baby. I desperately wanted to believe that she hadn't abandon me lightly, because if she did, this was the root cause of my anger. If she didn't, then I could probably come to terms with it all, but at the rate I was progressing, I would probably never know and all my questions would remain unanswered forever. My love for my adoptive parents had not lessened in any way, and I suppose that for some people, the pain of not knowing would have eased with time, but for me the quest had now become a lifetime's obsession. I couldn't help it – I was made like that. One of the problems I had was that I still felt as if I was the only adopted baby in the world. It was strange that although this was not the case, I just could not abandon that thought. I wondered then if other adoptees felt the same – in that case we were all members of the same club. The only problem with that idea was that there was no such thing as an adoptees' club!

A few days after the interview, the acting manager called me into the office and asked me to read the contents of a confidential document. It was a detailed report regarding the absence of the poor distraught girl, and the circumstances surrounding this matter. It was addressed to the district manager! So he was now acting as judge and executioner and his poison was about to reach new quarters. I did not have an antidote. My initial vibes had been correct about this man – he *was* untrustworthy. And with this thought, I made a resolution never to betray a confidence from that day onwards.

# Chapter XXIV

## LOOKING FOR ANOTHER SAMARITAN

1980 arrived and I once more took stock of my situation. This time I lay all the documents I had collected on my lounge floor. There was insufficient space, as I had accumulated so many. This was ridiculous, I thought – a grown man sifting and sorting through reams of paper, looking for a clue, trying to match one piece of information with another. But nothing yielded itself. I was always lacking at least one vital piece of information, and the most conspicuous item was my mother's date of birth. Without this I could move no further. I could continue to buy up more marriage certificates, but I had bought them all right up to 1966 and had established nothing. This part of the exercise was futile. I then decided to start looking further back and purchased a dozen birth certificates as far back as 1920. There were scores of Bridgett O'Neills, but none revealed information which I could use in my search. This was the proverbial needle in the haystack. One day, however, I overheard two of the staff at the bank talking about charities, and the good works carried out by certain charities. One of them was talking about her family.

'I managed to find my long-lost aunt three months ago – this was with the help of the Salvation Army.'

'I didn't realise you could do that,' replied the second girl, and upon hearing this comment, my ears pricked up. I listened carefully until the conversation was over and the more I thought about it, the stronger was my conviction that the Salvation Army could help me also. Slumber would not visit my eyelids that evening, and once more perplexing thoughts assailed my mind, until, worn out, I eventually fell asleep. I dreamed that the Salvation Army was about to reconcile me with my mother. I awoke to find myself defeated again but once more clutching to my old ally, hope. I looked up the head office of the Salvation Army and rang the number. I once again explained my dilemma and was then given another number, for the Family Tracing Service. I then telephoned this number and the voice at the other end sounded hopeful and positive.

'Yes, we can probably help you, John. Please write in with the information.'

I was ecstatic again; I had found another avenue by chance, and surely I could not fail this time?

My correspondence was addressed to the Salvation Army Family Tracing Service and was dispatched on a Monday. By Saturday a letter appeared on my mat and I knew it was their reply. Here I was again, almost shaking with excitement, about to open yet another important document. What would the contents reveal on this occasion? For the last five days, I had once again been courting hope – surely the stroke of luck I was so desperately seeking would yield itself. I tore open the envelope and began reading encouraging words.

> *Dear Mr Pickersgill,*
>
> *Thank you for your recent enquiry, in which you ask about the possibility of tracing your mother. It is noted that you were placed for adoption (or long term fostering) as a child.*
>
> *It is very natural that you should wish for information concerning your origins and we do understand the reasons which prompt your special request.*

I was growing excited and I closed my eyes as children might do, in order to perceive in the shining night of their own imagination, more stars than are visible in the firmament. Then I reopened them and stood motionless. I continued reading, but I could feel my brow darken more and more and I knew my lips and face were growing white as the blood drained away. Once again, anger seized my very being, not for the first time, and probably not for the last. By the time I had reached the end of the paragraph, the familiar tears were streaming down my cheeks. It continued: 'Unfortunately, however, we have to inform you that our programme does not include the tracing of natural parents in circumstances such as you have described, and we are therefore sorry to have to disappoint you.' The letter continued but I could not take it all in, and instead I began reading the A4 sheet which was also enclosed. There was a preamble about the adoption act, the usual standard stuff, but when I reached item three, I felt the anger swell up inside me and I let forth a tirade of abuse at everything and everyone I could think of. I shouted at the God I didn't even believe in; I cursed Providence and the demons that had once again returned to haunt me. I reread the first paragraph, and items three to six, and as I did so, I felt the same hurt which I had felt so often in the past, driving yet another pang into my heart. It read:

THE SALVATION ARMY SOCIAL SERVICES FAMILY TRACING SERVICE
Requests to trace a natural mother (father) on behalf of persons placed for adoption after birth;
    From time to time, this department receives requests from adopted people (adults) who would like us to trace their birth mothers (or sometimes fathers). Such requests, almost without exception, have to be declined, and we can well understand the disappointment which this causes. There are however, good practical and ethical reasons why the decision is taken.
1. Prior to 1976, when a mother placed her child for adoption, she was given to understand that the processes were carried out in confidence, and that approaches would not be made to her at some future time. As a responsible organisation, the Salvation Army takes the view that this understanding should continue to be honoured.
2. Very often, the details necessary for carrying out investigations are not available. A minimum requirement for the person sought is full present name, precise date of birth and last known address in the present country of residence. Frequently, the only details which are held concerning a birth mother are her maiden name, and address at the time her child was born.
3. In almost every case, our first contact with the person we are seeking is through the courtesy of a third party. This means that a letter explaining the purpose of our enquiry will be sent to someone else (perhaps an individual or an official organisation) who will not reveal an address to us, but who will forward our

correspondence to the person concerned. Once the communication has left our office, we exercise no control over who might open it, including a husband or grown-up children of the lady to whom it is addressed. This could cause great embarrassment and distress if they are not aware of the adopted person's existence. Whilst our desire is, wherever possible, to restore family relationships, we do seek to act in the best interests of all parties concerned, and not only in those of the enquirer. It would not be appropriate to try to help one person whilst at the same time bringing hurt and possible family disruption to others.

4. Frequently, with requests of this nature, we are asked to keep the enquiry secret from members of the adoptive family. This we could not agree to, since we must feel free in all our investigations to approach any one at all who might be able to assist. We could not, in any case, support a secretive search in this way.

5. In all our correspondence, we must be free to state the identity of the enquirer, the relationship to the person sought and the reason why the enquiry is being made.

6. In some exceptional circumstances, it may be possible to consider requests regarding siblings who were not placed for adoption, but only within the above guidelines, and not where the ultimate intention is to trace a birth mother. When we decline enquiries of this nature, we are not making a moral judgement with regard to character or behaviour, nor are we acting in an unchristian way. In most cases, the information which we require is not available, and always the risk of hurting others is great. As an organisation, we therefore have to take decisions in this area which may be unpopular. We do so with understanding and reluctance. It should be noted that we are not aware of any major agency in the United Kingdom which does pursue investigations of this nature.

This letter had been written by a director, the Director of Family Tracing, but I found no solace in the reasons given for their inability to help me. I had been led to believe that assistance was at hand, but this was not the case. In the space of several days my ally, hope, had revisited me, but had left me, once more, like a groom standing at the altar waiting for the bride who never appears.

Yet again my hopes had been dashed, and I was becoming a

broken spirit. I asked myself time and time again, why do people promise to help, and then never deliver that help when the time comes? There could be no doubt on this occasion that the man on the telephone had categorically stated I could be helped. But as usual I was becoming accustomed to empty promises.

# Chapter XXV

## A MISSING CLUE?

The trail was growing cold yet again and I convinced myself, therefore, that I had missed a vital clue. This time I laid out all the marriage certificates on the floor and began my repeated search. About a third of the way through the search something caught my eye and, immediately, I became seized like a man in a frenzy. Was I awake, or was it but a dream? For an instant, I leaned my head in my hands to prevent my senses from leaving me, and then I rushed madly about the room with wild cries until I returned to the document, still unable to believe the evidence of my senses. This time I fell on my knees and clasped my hands convulsively and uttered a 'prayer', to whom I did not know. I soon felt myself calmer and more happy, and now began to credit my felicity. How could I have missed such a vital clue?

Staring up at me from the green parchment was a date, a very significant date. It was the 30 September, 1950. This just had to be the vital link I had been searching for. It was far too much of a coincidence. Surely fate could not be toying with me again! The Bridget O'Neill named on this certificate had been married on my birthday, three years after my birth. I tried to put myself in her position again. Imagine giving birth to a child, subsequently giving that child up for adoption and then settling down after the pain and torment had subsided somewhat. It is most likely that a three-year period would have taken away a lot of the heartache, by which time one would be ready to get married. This just had to be correct or was I being fanciful? I now convinced myself that this was my mother, and that as the marriage date was so significant, perhaps after all she had married my father. Even if this was not the case, I felt certain that she had made a decision to get married, on the anniversary of my birth date. For one brief second I harboured a doubt, because the Bridget named on this certificate was spelt with one 'T', but this thought was dismissed as readily as it had come. That night I snatched only a few hours of sleep. The night was one of those delicious and yet terrible ones, and I couldn't wait until the next day to get started.

I had a strategy firmly fixed in my mind; I would visit the local library for the area named on the certificate, which happened to be Tooting, SW London. For once fate had been kind to me, as I worked only a short distance away from this postcode, at least if one travelled by car. When I made enquiries, however, I discovered that the voters' roll for 1947 onwards was held at Streatham. I arrived at the said library and the events began to unfold like a dream. I was carried along by the euphoria of it all.

I requested the voters' records and hastily turned the pages until the year 1947 appeared. I looked for Franciscan Road, which was the address I had extracted from the marriage certificate. Sure enough, I found the entry I was searching for, and listed were three names: George E Bennett, Frederick Bennett and Rose A Bennett.

The same occupants were listed again for 1948 and then, eureka! The entry for 1949 was the same, but with the additional name of Bridget O'Neill. Quickly I looked at the following year and, sure enough, there were the original three and now Bridget Bennett. Immediately my mind began building the picture. She had got into some kind of trouble. I wondered if *I* had been the trouble. Then she had gone to live with the Bennetts and married George in 1950. I couldn't get my mind round the next possibility. Was George Bennett my father? No, I told myself. Otherwise, why would I have been given up for adoption? Perhaps my mother had had a liaison with another man and then had met George E Bennett. I referred to the entries for the following years – they remained the same until 1956. That particular year, the entry for Frederick disappeared. He must surely have passed away. George, Bridget and Rose were still listed. Then the family scene changed again, for in 1957 the name on the voters' roll was just Rose Bennett. What, I asked myself, had happened to George and Bridget? But that of course was the wrong question to ask. The real question should have been: where had they moved to? A careful scrutiny of the following years revealed that Rose had lived on her own at that address until 1966, after which time the name Bennett disappeared from the records forever. Sadness once more took a hold, and would not be banished from my senses. I felt like a wounded man who trembles instinctively at the approach of the finger to the wound until it is healed. It felt as if my wound would never close, or that if it did close it would only reopen, in a more agonising way than ever. I once more considered myself the unhappiest of men, for I could find no way out of the maze I was lost in. I seemed to take one step forward and another one back. Where could I look next? I was becoming melancholy again, but at least I knew the reason: I did not have a clear sense of the past.

Another brainwave sprung into my mind and, as usual, it was another long shot. I had passed some sort of British Telecom museum near Blackfriars station. Perhaps I would find some sort of clue in the telephone archives records. What exactly I was to look for I could not be certain, but I would try anyway. I was hoping the Bennetts would be listed in the 1949 directory, and that thereafter I would find some clue to take me further forward. I realised I was clutching at straws, but desperate people tend to resort to desperate measures.

Looking up the entries for 1949 was easy, too easy, as there was no George E Bennett, or anything resembling it. Frederick, Rose and Bridget were not in the directory either. Of course there was no guarantee that they had been subscribers in those aeons so long ago. I moved my eye down the pages, and it was not until 1957 that any entry resembling that which I was searching for appeared. There were two entries registered for a George E Bennett, but both of them showed North London addresses. After that there were only three others, and the year relating to this was 1960. I soon decided that this course of enquiry would not offer anything constructive, and in some desperation I gave up.

# Chapter XXVI

# REFUSING TO GIVE IN

It was now October 1982 and I was a relatively young man of thirty-five years. But I was a lonely man, lonely for two reasons. I was no longer married and I lived on my own. Although I had a name, I had no identity. I felt like a shipwrecked person, alone on a desert island with no possible hope of rescue. I could visualise the rescue ship in the distance, but the vessel was always unable to land because it was on the wrong course through stormy waters.

There existed two John Pickersgills: the bold, accomplished character at work, and the fragile, sensitive individual lacking in both self-confidence and self-esteem. This cocksure person with his positive attitude was an achiever of the highest order in the workplace, but on a one-to-one with the opposite sex the confidence evaporated, leaving him looking like a sprinter in a marathon race.

Around this time, I was to attend a staff development course, which was to involve personality tests, most of which centred around personality strengths and weaknesses. I was not looking forward to this at all, as I was afraid the outcome would reveal character deficiencies which would mar my promotion prospects. When I sat down to start the test I was nervous for there were over three hundred questions. At the end of the assessment, an interview afforded me an opportunity to expand upon the information I had provided. It also enabled the interviewer to provide input, and form an opinion about the person he had interviewed. This opinion would be transcribed into a written report and passed on to a superior level. It was four o'clock when I entered the room for my interview, and the long and gazing search of my interviewer left me feeling cold and numb. After all, the answers I had provided had been interpreted by an occupational psychologist, and I wasn't sure what to expect.

'Good afternoon, John. Please be seated whilst we have our chat.' My interviewer spoke with the voice of a senior executive, with the rigid inflexibility of neck and shoulders which caused his inferiors to say that he was a living statue of everything the bank expected of a regional general manager. A few pleasantries were exchanged and then the interview proper commenced. 'Let's look at the individual areas to start with, and then I will offer an overall summary of how you fared in these tests.' He covered the nine characteristics and then gave me a description of the relevant 'ideal' qualities and skills. Then there was an embarrassed silence during which I was unsure about whether to speak or not. But the interrogator spoke first in his laboured manner.

'John, are you aware of what the bank is looking for from these tests?'

'Yes, I think so.'

'We are looking to find suitable candidates for senior management roles in the very near future. These assessments quite easily sort the wheat from the chaff.'

As he spoke those words, he gave me a steely glance and I felt my heart sink. I could feel the second John Pickersgill, the fragile sensitive character, rising to the surface. I desperately hoped that this would not show through. There was yet another long pause before he uttered his next words. I wondered what was coming – there appeared to be something ominous about his person. He was speaking slowly. Just get to the point, I thought, as this is dragging on.

'I have to tell you, John, that I have not seen results such as these for a long time.'

I no longer wanted to be in the room as I was now dreading the outcome. I was pretty sure my aspirations were about to be dashed on the rocks.

'The personality assessment reveals that you have weaknesses.'

Before he could continue I interrupted him. 'I see,' I replied.

Then he continued. 'It also reveals, however, that you have strengths. Would you like me to read them out?'

'Yes please,' I replied.

'Your strengths are revealed as someone who is very attentive to detail. You are a confident person and a persuasive speaker who is also articulate and fluent and a good listener. You are highly ambitious and have drive, enthusiasm and above all else an overwhelming commitment to succeed.'

I could scarcely contain myself, for this description did not appear to fit with the opinion that I had of myself. If I accepted these findings, surely I could take heart from this. I asked the question. 'There can be no errors with these tests, can there?'

'Not at all, John, as you gave the answers and these were interpreted by an occupational psychologist.'

'What about the weaknesses?' I wasn't sure I wanted to hear them, but my spirits had lifted quite considerably in the last few minutes and I felt as though I could accept any form of criticism at this moment in time.

'Although you are extremely self-confident, John, you may reveal your feelings too readily, and this could be perceived by the hierarchy as a weakness which could impinge on your career aspirations.'

So now I had the full picture, which I would analyse on the train back to London. Over and over I contemplated what the assessment had revealed, and it slowly sunk in that the tests portrayed the real person. Yes, I *was* prone to showing my true feelings all too easily, but there seemed little I could do about this. This was a trait I had inherited. As soon as that thought entered my mind, it was followed by the inevitable. Just who had I inherited this from, my mother or father? Then once again the yearnings stirred inside and I started asking myself further questions: what good is this doing, to keep mourning for my true parents, my true origins, in the secret recesses of my heart? Years of torment and grief had created an abyss somewhere in the depths of my heart, which would surely one day destroy me. I was judging myself with too much severity. I was a noble-minded person and I could not let my grief disarm me. I may have been abandoned by those who had created me, but I could not give up now. Suddenly, once more, the words of my interviewer came back to me, like a phantom in the night. 'You have an overwhelming commitment to succeed.' These were the last words he had uttered to me. How could I ever forget that? I felt myself driven on like an exterminating angel.

# Chapter XXVII
## DÉJÀ VU?

When in a reflective mood, I would ponder on the many strange coincidences which had unfolded in my life regarding the 'topic' of adoption. In the early days, it had seemed that I was the only adopted person in the world, but then I had been a child with childlike thoughts. But in adolescence and as a young man I had stumbled across not once, but three times, people involved in the adoption process. Whether by choice or otherwise, these people were involved in a major way in my everyday life. I had seen the argument from three different sides, four if I included myself. I had been plunged into the deepest misery, and yet I knew not why, and so I began to examine the past and the present, and I endeavoured to dive into the future by asking myself if this was all meant to be. If I was an actor in some sort of play, would it one day have an ending, a happy ending? If this were to be the case then perhaps I was a Divine Instrument. But just what was the Divine Instrument being used for? Was it to bring happiness to my adoptive parents? I had already done that – they were both proud of my achievements and proud of me as their son. Was I one day to find my real parents, be reunited and then make them proud of me? If that was to be the case, then I would have served the purpose of making several people happy, although not one hour of peaceful calm would I have had along the way. But I was being fanciful, for in the twenty-nine years since I had discovered the truth, my search had slowly ground to a halt. The best I could expect would be for me to trace my real mother – anything else would be a massive bonus.

He had been talking in the background to some of my colleagues, and now he came over to introduce himself to me.

'Good evening, John. I am very pleased to meet you.' This was my new area manager. 'Is your wife here also?'

'Er, no, I live on my own these days. I am divorced.'

'Oh, I am sorry to hear that. Do you have any children?'

'No, I suppose that was a blessing.' I wanted to divert the conversation away from myself, so I continued. 'Do you have a family?'

'Well, my wife is over there talking, and yes, we have two children. We have a son and a daughter, although our daughter is an adopted daughter.'

A cold shiver passed over the top of my shoulder blades and I tried to appear calm, although my inner self was shaking. In the space of eleven years, this was now the fourth time that this had happened to me, and always with my immediate superior, allowing for the one exception of my former wife. For once, however, I did not get the familiar déjà vu feeling. Was this another act of Providence, and if so, what was the purpose of it all?

'That's interesting,' I replied.

'What's her name?'

'Why do you ask?'

'Well, I am adopted too, so I always find this an interesting subject for discussion.'

'When she was just a few weeks old, someone offered me a bundle of clothes with a baby inside, and since then we have never looked back. She is twenty-six now, married with a family of her own.' I thought the conversation would reach a natural conclusion, but to my amazement he continued. 'Never once in all those years has she been a problem to us, for occasionally adopted children carry a chip on their shoulder, which can spill over into everyday life.'

I came in gingerly with my next question. 'You mean she has never worried about finding her true parents?' I was hoping I hadn't overstepped the mark.

'Why should she want to do that?' I felt sure that this last statement had been uttered with a tinge of contempt. It seemed as if I had suddenly touched a raw nerve, and I recoiled in case this became contentious.

'Some people might just feel the need to.'

'Well, our daughter has never wanted to trace her parents; she is quite happy with us. We are her true parents as far as she is concerned, and that is the way we like it. You have not contemplated looking, have you?'

I hesitated as I could sense the conversation might turn into an argument. 'Well, I have been searching for my mother for a long, long time, and I have made some progress, but my progress has been hampered just lately. I seem to have come to a dead end.'

'But you have got everything you need – a good job, health. Are your mum and dad still alive?'

'My mum is, but I lost my dad six years ago.'

'What more can you want? You don't need to go searching for anyone.'

'I need to find the real me, and I can only do that by finding my parents, at least my mother.'

'But she gave you away, so what's the purpose? It will be just a futile exercise.'

'It might not be, and I have made a resolve to keep searching until I can search no more.'

He turned on his heel and rejoined his wife. Not a very auspicious introduction, I thought. I will have to watch out for myself. I tried to deduce some sort of message from this latest meeting. Was there some higher element at work here? If there was, just what was the message? I couldn't find one, so now I looked at the situation from a statistical viewpoint. Of the four individuals I had met, and one of them had been my wife, only one had thought it correct to pursue my search. Two of them, at least, had had definite prejudices, and had wanted to discourage me from continuing the search. I began to question my motives, and of course myself. Can I have been tracing a false path? I asked myself. Can the end which I proposed be a mistaken end? Has one hour proved that the work upon which I have founded all my hopes is an impossible task, or even a sacrilegious undertaking? I could not reconcile my being to this idea – the more I tried to, the angrier I became. I thought very carefully about my situation. My position was like that of a person wounded in a dream; I could feel the wound, but I could not recollect when I had received it. With a monumental resolve, I reviewed my past life of sadness and I revisited the scenes where fate and misfortune had led me and where despair had received me. I needed to get the whole issue clear in my mind so I decided to drive to one of my favourite beauty spots, a little harbour on the East coast, where I could walk alone and think with clarity of mind.

The weather was magnificent, and the excursion a treat. The sun, red and flaming, was sinking into the water, which embraced it as it approached. The sea, smooth as crystal, was now and then disturbed by the leaping of fish which, pursued by some unseen enemy, sought safety in another element. On the extreme verge of the horizon, I could see fishermen's boats, white and graceful as the seagull, and several merchant vessels bound for the open sea. The whole scene was now becoming bathed in a golden light as I climbed the hillside above the harbour.

I wanted some sign, some revelation, and the remains of doubt to be removed from my mind. I wanted the feeling of sadness to be permanently wiped away and replaced by conviction. I proceeded back down to the quay, to where the pleasure boats were moored, and as I turned the last corner I spied an epigraph posted on the side of a building. It was advertising some sort of play. It read in large bold letters: 'The Taming of the Phantoms'. I immediately set off for home, thanking Providence for revealing itself.

# Chapter XXVIII

# A CONFIRMATION OF SORTS

A major part of my time had been spent searching, searching, searching. It was always a similar pattern. But the door would still not open. Five more long years passed and I reached the age of forty. Just where was my mother now? It was as if she had disappeared from the face of the earth after giving birth to me. Melancholy thoughts began to present themselves on a more regular basis. If I didn't find her soon, she might pass away and my efforts would have been wasted. However, I took some consolation from the fact that I was a very fit person. I still played soccer at a high level, climbed Scottish mountains and was generally a very good athlete. Assuming I had inherited these traits, there was a good chance she would still be alive and well. Conversely, such traits could have come from my father!

I was on business in my beloved Manchester, looking for the car park where I had left my car. Walking down a side street I read a sign above the doorway of what had once been a Lancashire cotton mill: 'GMCRO' (county archives). Imagine my elation! My spirits lifted and I went inside and up the stairs. Approaching the man behind the desk, who had the air of a librarian, I spoke.

'Good afternoon, can you help me? I am enquiring as to what sort of records you hold here.'

He pushed a compliment slip across the desk listing the types of records held. There was a list of eight as follows:

Central and Local Government, Genealogical, Family and Estate, Business, Manchester Ship Canal Company, Trade Union, Newspaper and Maps and Plans. On the reverse of this slip was a list of services provided, one of which was 'Helping People'. This was what I wanted to see. Perhaps they could help me? After I had explained my situation in the briefest of terms, the gentleman asked me to write to him, laying down exactly what it was that I needed to find. The records to Redcliffe maternity home would be the jewel in the crown: I dispatched my letter on the fifteenth of May. I had learned not to raise my hopes too much over the years, after so many disappointments and setbacks. But time after time new opportunities came along, and here another one was presenting itself. I would grasp this with both hands.

It always seemed to me that people took forever to reply, but on the twenty-fifth of May a letter dropped on to my door mat. Don't get too excited, I told myself and I slowly opened the letter.

*Thank you for your enquiry, received 16th May.*

*I have checked through our records, and have consulted the published guide to hospital records for Redcliffe Maternity Home, but without success. It is possible that the records for Redcliffe Maternity Home have not survived. This is not at all unusual, especially if the establishment was a private one. However I will keep trying and let you know if anything arises.*

*I am sorry not to have been of more assistance on this occasion and wish you well in our search.*

So now I had confirmation, of a sort, that the records had probably been destroyed. Once more a gloomy feeling took possession of my senses. Every time the crumbs fell from the table they were snatched away before I could take a mouthful, and I still remained hungry.

# Chapter XXIX

# ANOTHER RAY OF HOPE

Since I was struggling to make any headway on my own, I now resorted to reading every book I could find on both genealogy and adoption to help achieve a breakthrough. I contacted every association I could find, charitable and non-charitable, but the vital piece of information eluded me. Then in May 1991 a change in the law afforded me a little hope. The Children Act 1989 provided for the Registrar General to operate an Adoption Contact Register. In effect this meant that a register was created in two parts. Part one was a list of adopted people and part two was a list of birth parents and other relatives of an adopted person. The idea was to register your name in the appropriate section with the relevant details: the name in which your birth was registered before you were adopted, your date and place of birth, your birth mother's name and surname, and your birth mother's maiden name and birth father's name, if these were included in your original birth entry. If your birth mother then registered herself in part two of the register, then the authorities would write and inform you, as this was considered to be a 'match'. This was a very neat way of bringing people together after years of separation. Now I really did convince myself that this would be the last throw of the dice. I was running out of time and it was only reasonable to assume that opportunities would surely stop coming my way. I had lost count of the number of occasions fate had offered me a channel to pursue, always without success, but I had to strive forward and leave nothing to chance. I wanted the wheel of fortune to spin now in my direction, as I had become tired and weary over the years. I had almost worn a hole in my heart. I sent my details off to enable my name and address to be entered on the register. I had no way of knowing, whether my mother would even have heard of the Adoption Contact Register – that, of course, was allowing for the fact that she was alive and well. As usual a driving force from within drove me on. Obviously three things could happen. It was possible that I would obtain a reply quite soon, or it could be many years later, or, last of all, I might not receive a reply at all. I tried a session of positive thinking, *willing* a reply to arrive quite quickly. In my hearts of hearts I didn't really expect an immediate reply, but I lived in hope. Ten days after I had sent my details off, the postman delivered a letter and I recognised immediately from the envelope that it was from the contact register office.

Why was there a reply so promptly? This was too good to be true. There just had to be a match – there could be no other reason. I stared at the envelope, wanting to open it but hesitant to do so. My excitement reached a fever pitch. She was alive and had registered, I felt certain. She would have had no other way of contacting me, and she must have heard about this new system. At last all my hopes and aspirations were about to be realised! I wondered where she lived, and I lifted the envelope up to the light which revealed that there was a letter inside. It looked reasonably long from the bits I could see, and with that, I could contain myself no longer. I ripped open the envelope, tearing the letter slightly in my haste, and as I read the lines I felt the tears trickle down my cheeks once more. It merely read:

*Dear Mr Pickersgill,*

*I am writing to inform you that your name and address have been entered in Part I of the Adoption Contact Register in accordance with your request. Unfortunately, there is no relative registered on Part II at the present time. If/when a relative registers on Part II, their names and addresses together with the relationship will be sent to you at your address as shown above.*

*Should your wishes about making contact, or name/address change at any time, please inform this office in writing quoting the above reference number.*

*Yours sincerely,*

I had not read the small print properly, which told me that if no relative had registered, I would receive only an acknowledgement of my registration.

# Chapter XXX
# A TRUE ALLY

People in a situation such as mine are prone to doing a lot of thinking. I would tend to think not just about my birth parents, but also about whether I had any brothers or sisters and, if so, how old were they and what were they doing. I had been brought up an only child, and I often wondered what it would have been like to have shared an upbringing with others. If relatives such as these *did* exist, then they probably wouldn't know I existed, as it seemed unlikely that my real mother would have informed them. I assumed that I was a dark secret to be kept hidden away in the past, and the longer my search went on, the more prominent this idea became. Still, I remembered the vow I had made all those years ago. Whatever my findings turned out to be, I would accept them. The search for the real me, however, had almost ground to a halt, not because I had given up but because the myriad of passages had all led to a cul-de-sac.

September 1993, and I reached forty-five. Some sort of programme appeared on the television regarding adoption, and, as usual, I missed it. However, the next day it was reviewed in the national papers, and listed in those papers was the name and telephone number of an association for those interested in adoption and tracing their birth parents. I telephoned the number but I could not get through. It was constantly engaged. I was unsure as to whether this was a good or bad sign, but I opted for the former. I tried again the next day but without success, and yet again on the third day. This time I was connected. A cheery voice answered and explained that this was NORCAP (The National Organisation for Counselling Adoptees and Parents). This was a registered charity set up to assist people like myself who were desirous of finding their birth parents. I sent off my subscription and joined without hesitation. The sadness was once more expunged from my heart and my soul. Another combination of circumstances had presented itself at my feet for me to investigate. A detailed list was dispatched to me, explaining how I needed to proceed. However, my case was slightly different as I had spent nigh on thirty-five years searching in one way or another, and I had a lot of information to hand. What I needed was a guiding hand and advice about how to use this information in the best way. Because I had made quite a few inroads already, I was asked to forward all the documents I had accumulated to an intermediary named Carolyne. I was also asked to inform Carolyne of what action I had taken in the past to find my mother. Of course this involved me explaining the nature and content of the telephone call I had made all those years ago. I gave Carolyne a few days to digest the facts and called her to discuss the next move. In view of the very strange reply I had had to *the* telephone call, indeed the almost hostile nature of the response, we both decided that another visit to this lady would be worthwhile. The documentation and other fragmented bits of information suggested that the lady in question was at least a highly possible candidate. What was more, I checked that she still lived at the same address. Carolyne was a trained counsellor in this type of work and had been adopted herself. She took painstaking care to compose the correct letter, which was sent to the same Mrs McGowan I had telephoned so many, many years ago. The letter was sent in early October. It was courteous, sympathetic and understanding, written in such a manner that no one could have been offended. It was also succinct, explained my dilemma and gently referred to the telephone call which had taken place many years before. All this took place about six weeks after my joining NORCAP, and I felt for the umpteenth time that I was making progress again. About two weeks afterwards Carolyne rang me with some important news. I could hardly restrain myself while she began to relate her findings. She had received a call from Mrs McGowans' son, whom she described as a really nice, kind person, judging from his telephone manner. He had spoken briefly with his mother who didn't think she could help, but he now asked for further details, so he could investigate this more fully. He would look into the matter and return to Carolyne in the very near future with his findings. He did however explain that this was not a particularly good time for the letter to have arrived, as there was a family crisis in the background. Carolyne was fully convinced of the sincerity and tone of this young man. She requested that I be a little patient, for a reply was imminent. We were left slightly perplexed by his first remark, however, about his mother being unable to help personally. But perhaps this was too much of an ordeal for her, especially if this really was my mother.

I would just have to be a little more patient. Our approach had not been rejected, and I just assumed that this lady would need time to adjust. My convictions grew stronger – I felt sure we had found the right person. If I had been in her shoes and someone had turned up, out of the blue, forty-five years later, proclaiming to be my son, I would have reacted in one of three ways. I might immediately have admitted it, if I had the moral strength to do so. If I had not been the right person, then I would have just said, 'Sorry, you have got the wrong person,' and have walked away from the matter. Lastly, and this was the more likely scenario, I might not have wanted to admit to it straightaway, and therefore I would have offered some excuse, to play for more time. So this was my reasoning, also shared by my counsellor. Her reaction also tied in pretty well with the reaction I had received on the telephone way back in the late Seventies. If this was the wrong person a simple 'please leave us alone' would have sufficed, but I hadn't been rejected. This *had* to be encouraging!

# Chapter XXXI

## A STRANGE REACTION

If someone is ill a visit to the doctor will usually result in a cure. If someone has toothache a trip to the dentist will suffice. But if your mind or soul is tormented, then usually the cure has to come from within. What makes it worse, however, is if you are reliant on the frailty of another human being to provide the cure. Thus I found myself, in the autumn of 1993, waiting and waiting and waiting, like the desert traveller, hoping for the mirage to disappear so that the waterhole can be found. On numerous occasions I telephoned Carolyne, knowing deep down that the call would be futile. She had promised to call me as soon as she received news.

Time marched on. Christmas was looming and still there had been no word from the knight in shinning armour. I began to question the motives behind it all. Was this some sort of game? Was this a nasty trick being played on me, a punishment for having intruded into some other person's life? I wanted to send another letter, but for some reason Carolyne persuaded me that we must wait a little longer. Six long months went past, and still no word. Now I decided that this *was* my mother, but that she didn't want contact with me. This was a perfectly logical conclusion to reach – there could be no other explanation for the delay. All she had to do was confirm the facts, or just say, 'Sorry you have the wrong person.'

Now my feelings turned to anger, for this was no way to treat a fellow human being. It doesn't take a genius to work out the full extent of the wretched feeling that overwhelmed me. Unless this lady and her son were people of small ability, they would *know* just how important an answer was, and after all he had promised faithfully to reply.

Carolyne decided that she would contact the convent, again

back in Manchester, regarding the background to my adoption. Her reasoning was that as she was a trained counsellor and acting under the auspices of NORCAP, she might be able to extract the missing information more easily than I could. And still we waited. Carolyne now persuaded Sister Philomena, who was in charge of the convent, to try *personally* to locate the Redcliffe maternity home records, and, with them, my mother's date of birth. The first communication was made in April 1994, to the local authorities in Bury. No reply was forthcoming. A second and third request were made in May and June respectively, but there was not even the courtesy of an acknowledgement. My anger had stirred again and I then made a personal intervention. I telephoned the authorities personally, spoke to some imbecile and then demanded that I be allowed to speak to someone in authority. Now I was speaking to a high-ranking imbecile, a *supervisor imbecile,* but she promised to reply to Sister Philomena within the week. Without threatening in any way, I told her that I would be writing to the Chief Executive Officer if no answer was forthcoming. August arrived and neither I, nor the convent, had received a reply. Just how could idiots such as these hold down a job? It defied belief. We decided to return to these people at a later date.

On the eleventh of August, after an eternity of waiting, a second letter was posted to Mrs McGowan. She chose not to reply. We then decided by early November, to make one last plea, and on the third of November a final letter was dispatched. I had clung to the idea for over a year now that human beings had the greatest propensity of all creatures on earth to harm, and that that harm was usually directed to their fellow humans. A simple few words which would have taken only a few seconds to utter, or a few minutes to write down, would have eased the anguish of a fellow human who found himself in dire mental straits through no fault of his own. And still the dealer would not reveal her hand! The patience of Job was not in my make-up, and I was being tested to the limit. Being asked not to take drastic action was trying me to the bitter end, as I was the sad person at the mercy of some fellow human being. Then another quirk of fate appeared out of the blue. I decided it was a quirk of fate because the date was 8 December, 1994. This would have been the birthday of my late adopted father, who had died in 1981.

A letter arrived, but it was an unpleasant one, not from Mrs McGowan, nor even from her son, but from her daughter. Not one positive word could I find in the letter. It was written in a very negative tone. Her family had been having a stressful time, it said, and the last thing her mother wanted was a letter like this, especially when there were no real grounds for sending it.

'Surely you should have realised that by not replying, my mother had nothing to say?' she asked. Well yes, I didn't need to be a brain surgeon to work that out, but her refusal to reply to my letter did not answer my question. Was this my mother or not?

So now, fourteen months after the first letter, I still did not know with absolute certainty whether this person was my birth mother or not, because the lady herself had not replied specifically to my question. In fact she hadn't replied to a word – she had merely used her daughter as a mouthpiece. Now I was hoping that these were *not* my relations, as I didn't want to be related to people who treated others with contempt. This letter left a bitter taste in my mouth. It was written in a manner that suggested I was 'thick'. It suggested that I should have known that this could not be my mother. Well, unfortunately, reading the thoughts of other people was not a habit I had mastered, and now my anger would not subside until I had had my say. I immediately wrote out a letter.

*Dear Miss McGowan,*

*I have made this decision to write to you because of the tone of your letter to Mrs Carter. I am the subject of Mrs Carter's enquiry.*

*You refer to the 'untimely' letter. There are thousands of enquiries made each year by letter, and no person can possibly know when is a good or bad time to send them. I am sorry it was a difficult time for your family, but how are we to know?*

*You state that the letter was unwelcome; I am sorry but I do not understand your comments.*

*If your mother was not the person who could assist me, then surely a simple 'sorry you have the wrong person' would have been a normal reply. In my opinion, a letter of such a delicate nature can only be unwelcome (in some cases) if the recipient is the correct person being contacted. We certainly have not persistently followed up the enquiry as you suggest.*

*After the first letter was sent, Mrs Carter received a very under-standing telephone call from Mrs McGowan's son. He was very kind and promised he would telephone Mrs Carter back as soon as possible. Regretfully, he did not, hence both Mrs Carter's letter and now mine. I feel therefore that both these letters could have been avoided. You state that the questions are impertinent and irrelevant. I would like to assure you that they are neither impertinent nor irrelevant to me. They are vitally important to me!*

*The majority of the population, yourself included, have one distinct advantage that I do not. They all know their origins. I feel that as a human being I have the right (along with everyone) to know about my origins. It is sad that you cannot understand that. I am disappointed that Mrs McGowan was unable to reply herself, to Mrs Carter, and I realise that these enquiries can be surrounded with difficulties; but I have suffered with anxiety for a long while, and it is necessary to make these enquiries, and I shall continue to do so, until I reach a solution.*

*I am not expecting a reply to my letter as I merely wish you to understand the significance of the matter.*

*It is sad that your mother has not been in a position to help me.*

*Yours sincerely,*

*John Pickersgill*

I posted my letter without delay, and I immediately felt much better. I was not going to let a young girl have the last word, in such a distasteful manner.

I had a long discussion now with Carolyne and the consensus opinion was that we still did not know for sure. The only sure thing was that if this lady was my mother, then she did not wish to make contact. It was at this stage that Carolyne decided to introduce me to another person, a researcher who worked for NORCAP and their members on a voluntary basis. He had also been adopted and understood all the central issues and complica-tions surrounding adopted people. I was reliably informed that he had obtained some very good search results. All he asked for were the fees to cover his costs. I immediately set up a meeting at his home and took my case to him. His name was John Flood.

# Chapter XXXII
# THE DETECTIVE

It was apparent from our very first meeting that John Flood was an accomplished searcher. He gave me fresh hope. The fact that he too, just like Carolyne, had been through the same traumas as myself, and found his mother, reinforced my conviction that one day I might just discover the truth.

It was early 1995 when John set to work on my case, and as usual I was hoping for instant results, although I didn't actually say that to him. Four long months went by and I heard nothing. Then one day a letter arrived, quite a lengthy letter, and I was flabbergasted.

He had received, at long last, a reply regarding the archived electoral registers. The reply indicated that my mother had lived at a North London address at the time of my birth. This fact we already knew, but the latest information told us that no other family members had been resident at that address. This therefore was not her family home. At first glance this did not appear to take me any further, but unfortunately it did. The dates at which the registers were compiled were somewhere between 1945–1948, and in 1947 the voting age was twenty-one. To have been included on this register at this address (the address on my birth certificate), my mother would have had to have been born in 1925 or before. Two questions had been answered in one sentence, and I was immediately weighed down once more with a great sadness. This was startling information. It proved that Mrs McGowan could not be my mother as she was much younger, and secondly that she had not been lying to me. Getting an answer from her had proved incredibly difficult, and all these years later I cannot understand why the whole episode was shrouded in mystery. But now these latest findings added a new dimension to the jigsaw. I had always assumed that my mother had been a very young woman at the time of my birth. This evidence now proved that she was older than I imagined, and this made the search wider instead of narrower.

We were now left with two more time-consuming options. We could search the marriage indexes for all entries for Bridgett O'Neill from the last quarter of 1947 onwards, noting all possibilities and ordering certificates from those references. Well, I had already obtained most of these many years earlier – it just meant ordering some extra ones as we now knew my mother was older than I had first thought. We could try one more time to obtain information from the archived records of Redcliffe maternity home, even if only from an admissions register. I promptly asked John to undertake the latter, whilst I delved once again into the records at St Catherine's House. I achieved next to nothing whilst John was dealing once more with the convent.

He convinced Sister Philomena to consult their *legal* advisor, which was done, and she now personally contacted the Chief Executive of what was now Bury Health Care. She requested medical records for the maternity home, which would I hoped reveal my mother's date of birth or some other vital piece of information. On the 19 January, 1996, she received a reply.

*Dear Sister Philomena*
*Thank you for your letter dated 12th January, 1996, concerning John Pickersgill, formerly David O'Neill.*
*I am currently seeking guidance on your request and once this has been received I will write to you again.*
*Yours sincerely,*
*Chief Executive*

I found the whole thing incredible. This summed up the idiots in high-profile jobs, in a variety of professions. This time it happened to be the health service. Was this guy the Chief Executive or not? I thought chief executives were paid to make important decisions. This lunatic, the Chief Executive was taking *advice* on whether to *look* for the medical records of a maternity home, not at this stage to *release* them. If I had had his job, it would have taken me seconds to reach such a decision, because that is what I would have been paid for. It took this chief executive six weeks to reply, but at least a decision was made to make a search. The letter was as follows:

> Dear Sister Philomena
>
> I write further to my letter dated 19th January, 1996, concerning the above named. After an extensive search of our Medical Records Department, we have been unable to trace the medical records for a Bridgett O'Neill. I note that Mr Pickersgill was born in 1947 and therefore any records of his mother's, relating to his birth, would have been destroyed after twenty-five years, i.e. sometime around 1972.
>
> I am sorry that I have been unable to give you a more positive response.
>
> Yours sincerely,
> Chief Executive

So there we had it – there was no information available regarding myself or my mother from the Redcliffe maternity home. I couldn't see where we could move forward to from here, but also another problem had emerged from nowhere, just to confuse the issue. This was centred round the spelling of my mother's forename. All the data I had accumulated referred to 'Bridgett' spelt with a double 'T'. The lady residing in North London on the electoral roll of 1947 was 'Bridget' spelt with one 'T'. I discussed this at great length with John Flood. John's experience in such matters led him to believe that it was probably a red herring and that we should plough on regardless. Now it was time to order further marriage certificates, concentrating on the ages of the female party and hoping that one would reveal a Bridgett O'Neill whose occupation was entered 'chemist's assistant'. Nine more certificates arrived but none revealed any clue, and the research was costing me a small fortune. I tried to work out what the exercise had cost me to date, but I gave up after I had reached over two thousand pounds as it began to depress me. What a price to pay to find out the truth, to find the real me! But I had come too far now to give up the search, and the only thing which would stop me seeing this through to the end would be an act of

Providence. If anything happened to me before the end was reached, then at least I had tried – it would just be that my mother would never know. Time, of course, could also mess up my plans. The more the years went by, the greater the chance was that my mother would no longer be alive, but I chose to think positively and dismissed such gloomy thoughts from my mind.

# Chapter XXXIII

# IRISH CONNECTIONS

The search had from time to time left a mark on my emotions, and occasionally I was prone to what some may see as irrational behaviour.

A pink sun was sinking behind winter clouds as I pulled up outside the church. I wanted to revisit the church where I had last been some twenty years previously. Why I felt I needed to do this, I wasn't sure, but I was hoping to get a mental lift from the visit, as this was my baptismal church. I parked some way down the street and continued my journey on foot. Each step I trod oppressed my heart with fresh emotion. I arrived at the church door and entered. The font was still in the same position as it had been in all those years ago and at this spot, so pregnant with fond and filial remembrances, my heart beat almost to bursting. It felt as if my knees were weak, and a misty vapour floated over my eyes. I clung for support to the font and let the same memories and recollections drift into my mind. I listened once more to the words which my mother would probably have uttered until my thoughts were once more interrupted by the howling gale outside. An old lady was kneeling in one of the rows to the left of me, and she gazed with astonishment at the sight of this strange visitor's emotion. She must have wondered about me seeing the large tears silently chase each other down my stern and immovable features. But she must also have felt the sacredness of my grief, and kindly refrained from questioning me as to the cause. With instinctive delicacy, she left me to indulge my sorrow alone. When I withdrew from the scene of my painful recollections she accompanied me outside and politely asked, 'Can I be of any assistance?'

I thanked her. 'No, it's all right. I must be going now.' And I drove off into the winter night, with my thoughts.

Two more years elapsed. I was still buying up certificate after certificate but without success. Long discussions took place between John and me as to which was the best way forward. John felt that we should now take a different route and look into the Irish records in Dublin. I thought this was a great idea. In January 1998 he asked an experienced researcher based in Ireland to look at the records. But as per usual, relying on other people did not prove satisfactory. He did not receive the results he had expected. But over Easter he made a visit to Ireland himself, and made the time to visit the General Records Office in Dublin. He extracted from the birth indexes all the Bridget (and variants) O'Neill references, for the twelve years between 1914 and 1925 assuming this was a wide enough range to cover. He immediately wrote to me with his findings, and once more I took on the mantle of a saddened man. It was impossible to imagine the daunting task which now lay ahead. From the records one hundred and sixty-five entries appeared all bearing the name Bridget O'Neill. So Dublin appeared to be the place which held the key to the vault. But inside that vault was a labyrinth of passages, all leading in different directions, and of course we had no way of knowing which was the correct path to take. And to add insult to injury, none of these references showed the spelling as 'Bridgett'! The task now appeared insurmountable because of the sheer number of entries. And it was becoming extortionate. I was crushed under the weight of this latest blow for it would involve a trip to Ireland to purchase one hundred and sixty-five certificates, with an immediate outlay of about fifteen hundred pounds. I told myself that the cost was irrelevant, but the exercise seemed impractical and was not guaranteed to yield success. Now I really *was* unsure for the first time in all these years about what to do next. The clock was ticking away and I seemed unable to move forward. Providence had now deserted me. I had been led to the gates but I had not been allowed entry. A lifetime's search was about to end and the rigours of the search were about to defeat me. If life was a game, then I had been the toy. If life was a play, then I had merely been an extra, for I certainly did not have a leading part to play. I now desperately needed help and inspiration, and I wanted Providence (whatever that might be) to do for me, what I could not do for myself. It was now April 1998 and I was fifty.

# Chapter XXXIV

# A SHOT IN THE DARK OR PROVIDENCE CALLING?

John had casually suggested learning more about the occupants of the address at which my mother had been residing at the time of my birth in 1947. This was in case she had been staying with a relative, although we had previously concluded that this was unlikely. To be honest, I had overlooked this. Since I had been so focused on finding my mother, relatives had been a secondary consideration. I received a note from John: 'I think it could be useful to try and access the archived Electoral Registers for the years pre-and-post 1947.' It was late April and I agreed, and then I dismissed this temporarily from my mind. Very soon after this date I got another note from John. Between October 1945 and March 1952 the following people resided at the North London address:

| Electoral Register Date | Shown Resident |
| --- | --- |
| 15 Oct 1945 | Dorothea F K Sheppard & Ethel M Sheppard |
| 15 Oct 1946 | Dorothea F K Sheppard, Ethel M Sheppard, Norman W Lukyn |
| 15 Oct 1947 | Dorothea F K Sheppard, Cecilia Lukyn, Bridget O'Neill |
| 15 Oct 1948 | Dorothea F K Sheppard only |
| 15 Oct 1949 | Dorothea F K Grange, Horace Grange |
| 15 Mar 1950 | Dorothea F K Grange, Horace Grange |
| 15 Mar 1951 | Dorothea F K Grange, Horace Grange |
| 15 Mar 1952 | Dorothea F K Grange, Horace Grange |

On the surface it appeared that my mother had only been resident at this address for the one crucial period. In an attempt to clarify the relationships of the named residents, and to see if there was any family connection with Bridgett, we searched the marriage indexes at the Family Record Centre. It was noted that in the March quarter of 1940 there was an entry for Norman W J Lukyn's marriage to Cecilie M Sheppard, and in the June quarter of 1949 a Horace Grange's marriage to Dorothea F K Sheppard. Hoping to learn more, we ordered the certificates for both of these references, and awaited their arrival.

The first certificate indicated that C M Sheppard, a spinster, had married Norman Walter Joseph Lukyn, the son of Norman Howard Lukyn. The bride had had the same address as my mother, Bridgett O'Neill. The witnesses were identified as Ethel Sheppard and N H Lukyn.

The second one indicated that Dorothea Florence K Sheppard, a spinster, daughter of William Joseph Sheppard, had married Horace Grange, the son of Robert Grange. Both these parties had worked as clerical officers for the Tithe Redemption Commission. The witnesses to this ceremony were F W S Margrave, E S Felmer and C M Sheppard. Once again the bride had resided at the same address as Bridgett.

It seemed, therefore, that Bridgett (or Bridget) was living in October, 1947 with Dorothea, who married a work colleague, and Dorothea's thirty-two year old married sister, Cecilie Lukyn, whose husband Norman Walter Joseph Lukyn had lived at the same address the previous year without Cecilie. This looked complicated, but by using a little imagination it was possible to paint a picture. Whether or not this picture would help me remained to be seen.

So, we reasoned that the other resident in 1945 and 1946, Ethel M Sheppard, could have been the mother of Dorothea and Cecilie. This person had also been a witness at her younger daughter's wedding. John continued to sketch a picture in a manner which would have done Sherlock Holmes proud. If he was Sherlock Holmes, then at this particular time I was a mere Dr Watson. It could be further reasoned that the father of Dorothea and Cecilie, William Joseph Sheppard had died between 1940 and 1949, and there was a further possibility that their mother, Ethel M Sheppard had died between 1946 and 1947. Another singular fact stared us in the face. A witness at Dorothea's wedding was shown as C M Sheppard. Could this perhaps indicate that Cecilie had reverted to her maiden name, after a marriage break-up?

We tried to work out a sensible scenario but the picture became blurred again. Perhaps Bridgett had just taken a room with the family whilst pregnant in London. There did not appear to be any connection through work, and nor was there any apparent family connection. We obviously didn't know if Cecilie had had children, and we thought about looking at the birth indexes to see if that were the case. It just might have been that if Norman Lukyn was away at war, Cecilie had had an affair, and had been herself in a similar position to my mother. This could have been the connection.

As if it was a throwaway remark, John mentioned in the last two paragraphs of his latest correspondence to me that he had a couple of research tools and that he was about to use them. He wrote:

*With a couple of research tools I use, I have noted just one reference for a Dorothea Grange, resident at 4 Leamington Avenue, Southport, Lancashire. Should this be the same lady, she would now be aged 88. Shall we write to her, or her co-resident, Betty Hunt, to see if there may be some connection?*

'Most definitely,' I replied to John. 'There is nothing to lose.'

A further note read: 'Similarly, using the same tools, I have noted only one Lukyn reference, a Mary Lukyn resident at 36 Petersham Road, Richmond, Surrey. We may consider writing to see if there is any connection with Cecilie and Norman.' John dispatched a sincere, kind and understanding letter, on 11 June, 1998, to the said Dorothea Grange, asking if this lady could assist. The details politely stated that on behalf of a friend of his, he was trying to locate, or at least learn more of, Bridgett O'Neill. He hoped she was the lady in question, if not, could she offer any ideas at all? I had grown used to a lifetime of disappointments and did not allow myself to get ecstatic, for this was truly an avenue with a very slim chance of success. I for once did not let the matter dominate my thoughts.

# Chapter XXXV

# A DAY TO REMEMBER

Many people remember dates at the drop of a hat, without even having to think about them. Others will struggle and may have to look them up in a historical reference book. But most of the world's population will remember the significant dates, such as the dates of the world wars, or a famous battle date, maybe 1066, or 1215, the signing of an important charter. But these are generally facts, which are taught to us usually at school. Ask an individual to remember a date or time or an important event in his or her personal life, and they will almost certainly be able to recall it without hesitation. If they cannot remember the date, they will be able to describe the time, the day or the event with the most vivid clarity. Remembering dates in *my* past life had always been child's play, and when asked to describe past events, I could immediately assume the role of an artist with the greatest of ease. There had been several significant dates in the past, some of which had uncanny connections. The twelfth of January 1965 had been the date that I had first joined the bank. The twelfth of January 1982 had been the day my ex-wife had gone to live on her own.

For those who strive or suffer or yearn, the fire may never go out. The pain may never lessen and they may never get out of the abyss. The voice in their hearts is sorrowful, and points out the future in unhappy colours. Do any of us know what determining factors allow some to be successful, allow some to be released from their chains, whilst others remain with weakened minds, seeing everything through a black veil? Does the soul form its own horizons? Does a soul that is darkened always see the sky of the future as stormy and uncompromising?

Does the soul that is lightened see the future as calm and with peace? Well, until the day that Providence decides to reveal the future to all mankind, none of us will know.

But the one thing that is certain is that the longer Providence delays deliverance, then that deliverance, when it falls, falls far more effectually. And so it was with me. A day which will forever be imprinted in the inner recesses of my mind and soul. A day when the devouring thirst was about to be quenched, a day when the fatigue and weariness were to be replaced by a desire for acceptance. It arrived without warning. It was 10.30 in the morning, 20 June, 1998. I had hardly rinsed the sleep from my eyes when the telephone rang. It was John Flood.

'John, are you ready for a shock?'

I immediately thought he had some bad news to give me. 'Well yes, what do you have to tell me?'

'You are aware I wrote on your behalf to a lady by the name of Dorothea Grange. Well, I have received a reply to my letter this very morning.'

My ears pricked up and I was listening very attentively, unsure as to what was to follow.

'Dorothea, I am afraid, died two years ago.'

When he spoke these words my heart sank. This was going to be another fruitless search.

'This letter, however, is from a Miss B Hunt, who apparently was Dorothea's niece-in-law. Let me read it to you: Dear Mr Flood, I am sorry to have to inform you, that Dorothea Grange died almost two years ago and therefore is unable to assist you. However, I am her niece-in-law, and I have spoken to the lady you are trying to trace, Bridgett, on your behalf, and she says you may contact her, either by telephone or by letter, at the address below. Yours sincerely, Miss B Hunt.'

A thousand things flashed before my eyes, and my mind became overloaded with thoughts. I was seized with vertigo. And then one overriding thought grasped my mind. She was alive! Now I struggled to do battle with my emotions, for I was on the verge of tears. And yet I had learned nothing, save that the person who had given me life was still here on this planet, somewhere. Can you imagine what was happening to me? The jailer had approached my prison bars to announce my reprieve, and had now inserted the key in the lock. I was seated on my stool in the corner, still handcuffed to the prison walls. All that I was waiting for now was for the chains to be released from my body and the prison door to be flung open: I would then walk free to the outside world. I gathered my emotions and muttered a few words to John.

'I can scarcely believe what you are telling me, she is still alive!'

'Yes, and hopefully she will be expecting a call from me.'

'What do we do now then?' I asked.

'I will call her today and, if I make contact, call you back straightaway.' With that he rang off. This treasure trove, which had just been found, was more valuable than the richest jewel on earth, and I spent the rest of the morning in a daze. The afternoon arrived and there was still no return call. Now the suspense was becoming too much. I was growing anxious. This was only the beginning. What if John had made the call and the response had been negative? Fifty years of anguish and torment could be dashed at a stroke, but I refused to let my mind dwell on such melancholy. I had come too far, overcome so many trials and tribulations, to be defeated at the last hurdle. I would wait with a positive heart. Early evening arrived and still the phone would not ring. I was tempted to phone John, but I resisted. It had taken fifty years to reach this point – another few hours or days would not affect the outcome so greatly. Thoughts from the past entered my mind continually, but like the country through which we walk, they became indistinct as the time wore on.

At 6.30 p.m. the phone rang. I picked up the receiver nervously.

'John here. It would probably be best if you are sitting in a comfortable position.'

I wasn't sure if he was joking, but his voice didn't sound negative. 'I called you earlier but you must have been out.'

'Yes, I was for a while.'

He began. 'I spoke with Bridgett earlier today, and at the beginning of the conversation she did not recognise the reason for my letter, guessing instead that it concerned either Dorothea or her sister, Cecilie. As the conversation progressed I mentioned David O'Neill and then the penny dropped. Without acknowledging the fact that she was indeed the lady we were seeking, she asked a number of questions regarding myself, the organisation I worked for, the basis under which I worked and then about yourself. A certain amount of confusion arose, as both you and I are named John, and I think she initially thought that I might be you, talking to her under an alias. I only referred to you as David, now known as John. When Bridgett asked me your surname I told her it began with the letter "P", at which point she told me that it was Pickersgill. Now I was quite certain I was talking to your birth mother, and the conversation continued from there. Bridgett said that although she was shocked by my approach, she was delighted that you had found her, and sends you her fond regards.'

Overcome with emotion I kept asking questions, but at the same time my mind could only take in one fact. She was alive and of good health in mind and body. During all the difficult times, I could have given up my search, yielded to the burden of my task, but I had launched myself out into the path that had been opened to me: I had overcome every obstacle and reached the goal. Now it would be left to my mother to respond, and over that I would have no control. At seven thirty my lifelong friend from school arrived from Manchester with his wife for a weekend visit. We had known each other forty-six years and had shared so many experiences together that we were like inseparable twins. He knew all about my search and, although he never commented, he must have seen from time to time the mental strain that this lifelong search had placed upon me. I told them the news and they also could hardly contain themselves. Then Susan and I uncorked the champagne and the four of us drank our way into the following morning, with boisterous revelry.

# Chapter XXXVI

# LIVING WITH PATIENCE

Now it was time to allow my mother to take it all in. How would she respond? My fear now was that I could still be rejected. Surely Providence would not play such a cruel trick on me, at this stage? Perhaps not, but Providence still had one card to play, as if to say to me that the game was not quite over yet. A game? This was not a game, but it *was* a test of resolve, and now it was turning into a game of 'Patience'.

Bridgett was about to leave for a month's visit to the States. A month, a whole month. I would be left in limbo. Then I remembered the final words of John's call to me: 'Just a little more patience required!'

I decided I would trust in patience and immediately I was rewarded. It was Wednesday, the twenty-fourth of June, four days after the 'event', and a letter arrived from Bridgett. It was poignantly written. She was still shocked, and it was sad that contact had to be this way. She would find the courage to meet me upon her return from the States. These few lines told me all I wanted to know. All my trials and tribulations had been overcome, the demons exorcised, and my victory was nearly almost won. I examined the date of her letter, twenty-third of June 1998. I felt a shiver down my spine. It was seventeen years to the very day since my adopted father had died, aged sixty-one. Was he looking after me?

The final week in July arrived and I still hadn't heard from Bridgett. Now I was having doubts. Perhaps she had changed her mind. No I refused to accept that. There had to be another reason. I had sent a little note in response to her letter, via John Flood, and I knew he had received it. I rang him.

'John, I have heard nothing, and Bridgett must have returned from the States by now.'

'I am sure she promised to come back to me, on your behalf,' he replied. He promised to telephone her for me. This waiting was interminable. If she had changed her mind, I would have been unable to take it. Just what was going on? I could not imagine Bridgett, nor myself, making empty promises – it was not in our genes. I could not have come this far only to fall at the finishing post. The phone went again; it was John.

'Just a misunderstanding. Bridgett is waiting to hear from you, I thought she was to make first contact on her return. I held on to your letter because of that, but now I have dispatched it immediately.'

Things were now back on course and I rested a little easier. It was Wednesday 5 August at six o'clock. I answered the telephone.

'John, this is Bridgett.'

This was the first time I had ever heard her voice! It was not how I had expected her to sound, but so what? This was one moment I had been waiting for for fifty years! I was now talking to my birth mother. I had not been prepared for verbal contact. I was about to struggle for something to say, but there was no need because Bridgett was talking. She was confident and I too was confident, and this first conversation was so natural. Now we arranged for me to visit her on the following Tuesday. But the following day this was hastily brought forward to Saturday, just two days away. I thought hard about what I should say or what I shouldn't say, but this was a useless exercise which I could not get my brain around. In the end I decided that whatever came out would just come out.

The fateful day had arrived. Could anyone imagine what this day meant to me? Could the most intelligent of beings understand the feelings in my heart? I hoped that this would be the day when I would be set free at last. This would be the day when John Pickersgill and David O'Neill would become one. I had been down in the depths and now I was to scale the heights. I had been true to myself for fifty years.

I had carried on when all hope was lost; I had believed when others had not. The fruits of my labour were about to be harvested, and at last I had some pride in myself. In my opinion what I had achieved could not be measured in human terms.

Emotions of such magnitude could only be felt and understood by the two parties concerned, albeit from different viewpoints.

It was a scorching hot day, and I felt quite relaxed while I drove over to Bridgett's, carefully scrutinising the map she had sent me. Not once did I go wrong, and I pulled up outside her drive bang on time. Now I was feeling tense, but I was in control. I wondered how Bridgett was feeling. For some strange reason, I hoped that she wouldn't come rushing out to greet me. I wanted to approach the front door with ease, ring the bell and then allow her to come to the door in her own time. This is exactly what happened and I felt better for it.

She opened the door with a warm greeting and welcomed me inside. No one can predict a scene like this, least of all the two parties concerned. Fifty years of intimate emotions want to be released in several seconds and it is not possible for that to happen. It has to be released slowly and freely, otherwise it is not natural, and therefore for the first few minutes both of us were in strict control of our emotions. We had already exchanged photographs and this helped us both in the build-up to those first intimate moments. The morning passed so very quickly, and as there was so much to discuss we both kept jumping from one subject to another, interrupted only by the tears of emotion which from time to time rolled down our cheeks.

# Chapter XXXVII

## THE RECITAL

My mother described the whole event as a 'sad, sad happening'. Having been posted to an RAF base in the Far East, she found herself pregnant in a foreign country with my English father renouncing any responsibility. But what made it worse was that she was an unmarried Catholic mother, and in those days society was intolerant of young women in that situation. As she was explaining this, I thought back to all those years ago, and to the conversation with my kind old manager. I remembered it vividly; we had been discussing the reasons why a mother would want to have a child adopted, and now I knew. The family and social pressures were one reason and, secondly, my mother had been abandoned by my father! When she broached the subject with him, he denied all knowledge, and she was then left to make a decision alone. She chose to give me life and returned to England for my birth. She had been working with Cecilie Lukyn overseas and it was this connection which had taken her to North London, to stay for a short while with Dorothea. She then travelled to Manchester for my birth and returned to London. The only strange addition to this part of the story surrounded my baptism. I asked Bridgett who Kathleen Cunningham was, one of the witnesses at my baptism. She looked puzzled.

'John, I didn't take you to be baptised, I left you in the capable hands of the nuns.'

This little mystery remains unsolved, as my mother has never known anyone by the name of Kathleen Cunningham. All I can surmise is that this mysterious person had been one of the nuns, although how Bridgett came to be a witness to a ceremony she did not attend can never be solved. I explained all the setbacks I had suffered and how I had been longing to discover her and indeed my father but most of all my origins. She had thought about me often, but the authorities had gone to great lengths to point out that once you had given up your child for adoption, there could be no turning back. That was an absolute fact.

Now that I knew the story I wanted to learn about the traits I had inherited. There were many. My love of the mountains, my musical abilities, my stature and the texture of my skin – the list was endless. We laughed out loud together at one point, because I also have an innate ability to complain if the service I receive is shoddy, which is also a characteristic shared by my mother. One of the most important findings for me, however, was that at seventy-eight she was in remarkable health in both mind and body and I was very much hoping that this would be passed on to me. We now examined photographs from those days gone by, with Bridgett poignantly describing how she remembered me in my first few weeks on earth. A small bundle but radiating good health – not the description given to me by my adopted parents, who had described me as a 'Belson baby'. Perhaps I had been wasting away in the convent in the first few weeks. So now we had got through the most traumatic part of the day and our stories were unearthing our true selves. We were coping with it all in a very caring but empathetic manner. I had often wondered what would happen if one day we reached this stage and then despised each other. In this age of freedom so alien to the period I was born in, I may have turned out to be a roguish lout, hell-bent on revenge, whilst my mother could have been a cold-hearted woman, devoid of feeling. But that just could not have been, as long as I applied my beliefs, as I had done from the very beginning when I had been just a small child. And I remembered my words well for I had uttered them many times on this journey.

I believed that characteristics were in the genes and not gleaned from one's adopted parents, and now I had proved this.

We meandered down the country lanes in the roasting afternoon sun to a reservoir, which was full of wildlife. It all felt so natural, a far cry from the cold winter evening I had spent at the church in Rochdale. The sun was setting in a blaze of glory as if to set the seal on this momentous day when I had learnt such a lot. It seemed to me that Bridgett felt sad that she could not shed any light on the whereabouts of my father. But he had deserted her, and in effect, me also. The likelihood of me ever getting to meet him was remote, and that was assuming he was still alive. But at least I had seen a wartime photograph, and for that I was thankful. While I was unaware of the traits I had inherited from him, to know what he looked like was helpful, even though I carried the looks of the O'Neills. The day was almost over and we walked back to the house for our final chat of the day. Then I gathered together my accumulation of documents, which astonished Bridgett. Never had she seen so many items and never had she met anyone with such dogged determination and courage. But that courage was not all mine alone, and I decided to coin a phrase of my own: 'Like son, like mother'. For truly my mother had shown exceptional courage throughout her life in dealing with my birth and the events thereafter.

# Chapter XXXVIII

# A NEW FAMILY

My mother handled my birth and the trauma surrounding it single-handedly. She came home from the Far East for my birth, at a time when society frowned upon such events. She confided only in her sister and her friend Dorothea and then returned once more to work abroad. It was there that she met and married her husband, and she was now a seventy-eight-year-old widow with four children. Four children! So now I had blood relations: what if they rejected me? I was a stranger about to intrude in their lives – this could stir up all sorts of problems. Then how would they react to their mother? Can anyone imagine the burden that this lady, my mother, had carried around with her for almost a lifetime? This secret she had kept to herself, not wanting to burden others with the complexities of it all. Now that takes great courage, the greatest of courage that mankind can find. Not once, but on four separate occasions, she had voluntarily chosen to relate the sad circumstances surrounding my birth to her children, my half sisters and brother. Yes, I now had three sisters and a brother. I had discovered my mother; would I now be meeting my 'real' relations? If my theory on the inheritance of characteristics was correct, then I had no reason to suppose that I would not be accepted. This was about to be put to the test.

It was hard to describe the feelings which arrested my very being over the next few weeks. One by one I received welcoming notes from my new family, including Bridgett's sister, the only other person to see me as a baby. If I had complained about lack of self esteem in the past, then here were some seeds to help make it grow. Family meetings were arranged and I was welcomed into the family. The wounds in my heart were beginning to heal. Photographs taken of me side by side with my brother and sisters reveal common characteristics. This was like a new world for me, and yet it felt as if I had known them all my life. They were ordinary people going about their lives when they had suddenly been asked to accept a total stranger as a brother. They did so without hesitation, and for that I shall be eternally thankful.

Often I have looked back and thought about the way things could have turned out. She could have spurned my approach, and who could say how I would have reacted then? But no, she had welcomed me into her life without any pressure from me – the decision had been left entirely to Bridgett. It is tempting for any adoptee to want to make immediate contact when your mother is found but I waited and allowed Bridgett her own space. After a lifetime of searching, another few weeks were not going to make such a difference.

Curiosity lurks in the minds of most of us, and out of the very few people who actually know the situation, several have asked if things are different for me now. The lifetime's struggle with oppression is over and I have, like the Phoenix, risen from the ashes. From captivity and solitude I have been restored to light and liberty. I have found the answers to a lot of my questions. This has made the fight worth it all, the journey complete, but out of the victory roll, other questions now come to the fore. Are we all divine instruments of Providence, or is everything just brought about by mere chance? My adoption offered a lifetime's happiness to my adopted parents who were unable to have children of their own, and I received a strict but normal upbringing to prepare me for adult life. My natural mother welcomed me with open arms and therefore John Pickersgill has brought happiness to both parties, albeit at different ends of a lifetime. If I examine the facts very carefully, I am left with two distinct lines of thought. Some would say that my sheer act of persistence was bound to achieve a result in the end. A man who persists is more likely to succeed than he who gives up at the first hurdle. Others have indeed said to me that it is all down to chance. My mother was born in Ireland but never lived there, and when she returned abroad after my birth she eventually married in a foreign country. In essence, therefore, this meant that there were no records available here for me to search. Her marriage is not recorded in the records at St Catherine's House, which was the crux of the whole problem.

The most important piece of the puzzle had always been missing. So now I am left with two choices. Do I consider the letter we sent to Dorothea Sheppard as an act of Providence, or a mere chance in the dark? Well, the chances of finding my mother without this tenuous connection were nil and I am not a spiritual person. Therefore I can only let the reader decide. Perhaps those reading this story will find many parallels in their own lives. Well, if my narrative can help people relate to events in their own lives so much the better. It will have served yet another useful purpose. And as for John Pickersgill, who has now found one half of himself, is no longer looking for the real me!